PRIMARY MATHEMATICS

Standards Edition

1

EXTRA PRACTICE

Tay Choon Mong

Marshall Cavendish
Education

© 2008 Marshall Cavendish International (Singapore) Private Limited
© 2014 Marshall Cavendish Education Pte Ltd

Published by Marshall Cavendish Education
Times Centre, 1 New Industrial Road, Singapore 536196
Customer Service Hotline: (65) 6213 9688
US Office Tel: (1-914) 332 8888 I Fax: (1-914) 332 8882
E-mail: cs@mceducation.com
Website: www.mceducation.com

Marshall Cavendish Corporation
99 White Plains Road
Tarrytown, NY 10591
U.S.A.
Tel: (1-914) 332 8888
Fax: (1-914) 332 8882
E-mail: mcc@marshallcavendish.com
Website: www.marshallcavendish.com

First published 2008
Reprinted 2009, 2010 (twice), 2011, 2012 (twice), 2013, 2014, 2015, 2016, 2018, 2019

Primary Mathematics (Standards Edition) Extra Practice 1
ISBN: 978-0-7614-7002-1

Printed in Singapore

Preface

Primary Mathematics (Standards Edition) Extra Practice is a series of five supplementary books.

This series follows the topical arrangement in the Primary Mathematics (Standards Edition) Textbooks and Workbooks. Friendly Notes at the beginning of each unit provide a source for reference and revision of concepts. The level of difficulty, as well as the style of the problems, is similar to the exercises in the Textbooks and Workbooks. The short and topic-specific exercises enable instructors to assign work only in those topics in which the student needs more practice. This, together with the simple language used, allows students to review mathematics with minimal guidance.

Primary Mathematics (Standards Edition) Extra Practice aims to consolidate and reinforce the mathematical skills taught in the Primary Mathematics series. Students will master mathematical concepts with confidence through the use of this series.

Contents

Unit 1	**Numbers 0 to 10**	1
Exercise 1A	Counting	3
Exercise 1B	Counting	5
Unit 2	**Number Bonds**	7
Exercise 1	Making Number Stories	9
Unit 3	**Addition**	13
Exercise 1	Making Addition Stories	15
Exercise 2	Addition with Number Bonds	17
Exercise 3A	Other Methods of Addition	19
Exercise 3B	Other Methods of Addition	23
Exercise 3C	Other Methods of Addition	25
Unit 4	**Subtraction**	27
Exercise 1A	Making Subtraction Stories	29
Exercise 1B	Making Subtraction Stories	31
Exercise 2A	Methods of Subtraction	35
Exercise 2B	Methods of Subtraction	37
Exercise 2C	Methods of Subtraction	41
Unit 5	**Position**	43
Exercise 1	Position and Direction	47
Exercise 2	Ordinal Numbers – Naming Position	49
Unit 6	**Numbers to 20**	51
Exercise 1	Counting and Comparing	55
Exercise 2A	Addition and Subtraction	59
Exercise 2B	Addition and Subtraction	61
Exercise 2C	Addition and Subtraction	63
Exercise 2D	Addition and Subtraction	65
Unit 7	**Shapes**	69
Exercise 1A	Common Shapes	73
Exercise 1B	Common Shapes	77
Unit 8	**Length**	79
Exercise 1	Comparing Length	81
Exercise 2	Measuring Length	83
Unit 9	**Weight**	85
Exercise 1	Comparing Weight	87
Exercise 2	Measuring Weight	89
Unit 10	**Capacity**	91
Exercise 1	Comparing Capacity	93
Exercise 2	Measuring Capacity	95

Unit 11	**Comparing Numbers**	97
Exercise 1A	Comparing Numbers	99
Exercise 1B	Comparing Numbers	101
Exercise 2	Comparison by Subtraction	103
Unit 12	**Graphs**	105
Exercise 1A	Graphs	109
Exercise 1B	Graphs	111
Unit 13	**Numbers to 40**	115
Exercise 1A	Counting	123
Exercise 1B	Counting	125
Exercise 2	Tens and Ones	127
Exercise 3A	Addition and Subtraction	129
Exercise 3B	Addition and Subtraction	133
Exercise 4	Adding Three Numbers	137
Exercise 5	Counting by 2's	139
Unit 14	**Multiplication**	141
Exercise 1	Adding Equal Groups	143
Exercise 2	Making Multiplication Stories	145
Exercise 3	Multiplication Within 40	147
Unit 15	**Division**	149
Exercise 1	Sharing and Grouping	151
Unit 16	**Halves and Fourths**	153
Exercise 1	Making Halves and Fourths	155
Unit 17	**Time**	157
Exercise 1A	Telling Time	159
Exercise 1B	Telling Time	161
Exercise 2	Estimating Time	163
Unit 18	**Numbers to 100**	165
Exercise 1	Tens and Ones	175
Exercice 2	Estimation	179
Exercise 3	Order of Numbers	181
Exercise 4	Comparing Numbers	183
Exercise 5	Addition Within 100	185
Exercise 6	Subtraction Within 100	189
Unit 19	**Money**	193
Exercise 1	Bills and Coins	197
Exercise 2	Shopping	201
Answers		203

© 2008 Marshall Cavendish International (Singapore) Private Limited

Primary Mathematics (Standards Edition) Extra Practice 1

Blank

Unit 1 : Numbers 0 to 10

Friendly Notes

Counting Numbers

We can count on from 0 to 10.
We can also count backwards from 10 to 0.

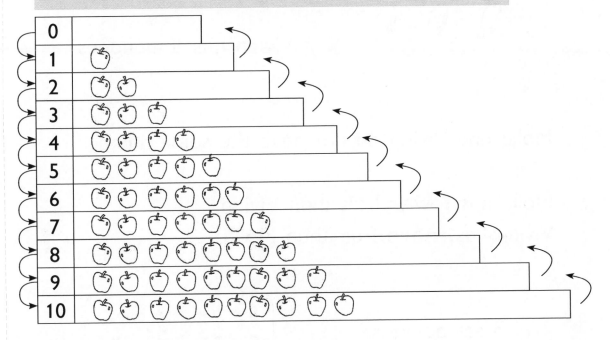

Writing Numbers in Words

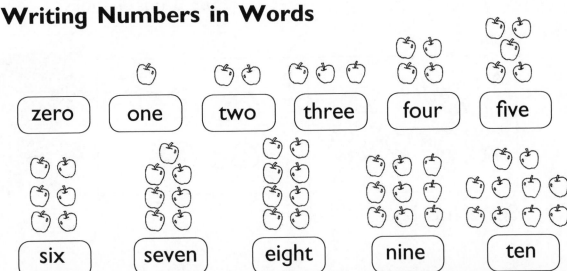

zero   one   two   three   four   five

six   seven   eight   nine   ten

Primary Mathematics (Standards Edition) Extra Practice 1

Comparing Numbers

 Molly has 4 apples.

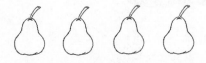 Sue has 4 pears.

Molly and Sue have the **same number** of fruit.

 Vivian has 6 mangoes.

Molly and Vivian do not have the same number of fruit.
Molly has **fewer** fruit than Vivian.
Vivian has **more** fruit than Molly.

Which set has less?

Set A has 6 bees.
Set B has 4 snails.

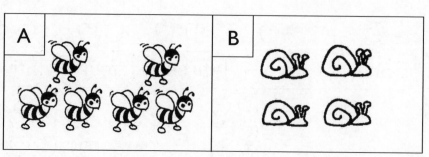 

Set B has less.

Primary Mathematics (Standards Edition) Extra Practice 1

Exercise 1A : Counting

1.   Match.

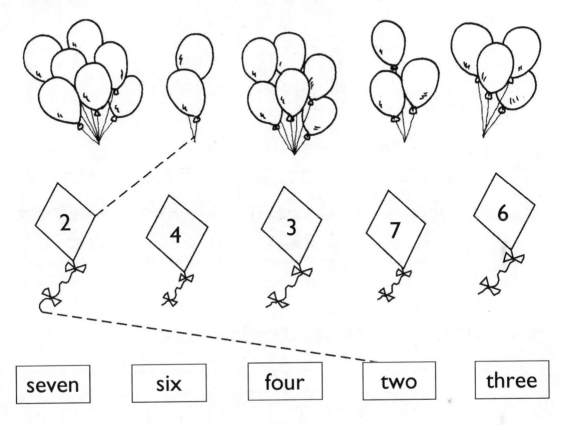

seven   six   four   two   three

2.   Write the correct number in the box.

(a)   (b)

(c)   (d)

3. Circle the two sets which have **the same number** of objects.

(a)

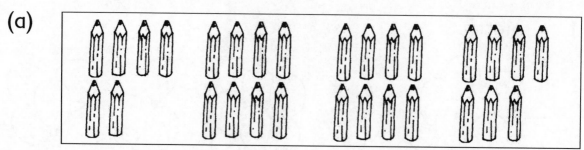

(b)

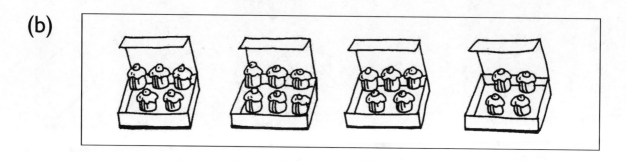

4. Check ✔ the set that has **less**.

5. Check ✔ the set that has **more**.

Primary Mathematics (Standards Edition) Extra Practice 1

Exercise 1B : Counting

1. Color the correct number of objects.

(a)

7 seven	

(b)

3 three	

(c)

9 nine	

(d)

5 five	

(e)

2 two	

Primary Mathematics (Standards Edition) Extra Practice 1

2. Join the dots in order. Begin with 1.

(a)

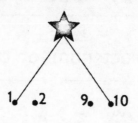

1.   .2   9.   .10

3.   4   7.   .8

5.   .6

(b)

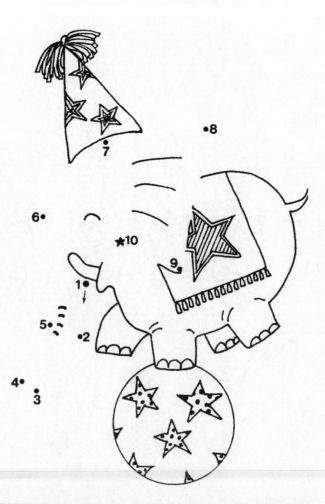

Primary Mathematics (Standards Edition) Extra Practice 1

Unit 2 : Number Bonds

Making Number Stories

There are 6 children.
2 are boys.
4 are girls.

2 and 4 make 6.

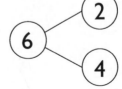

4 and 2 also make 6.

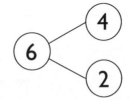

2, 4 and 6 make a number bond.

What other pairs of numbers make 6?
Let us take a look at these number bonds.

 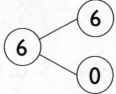

6 and 0 make 6.

 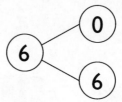

0 and 6 make 6.

 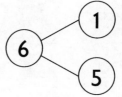

1 and 5 make 6.

 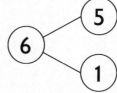

5 and 1 make 6.

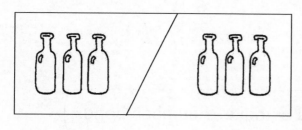 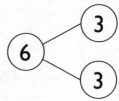

3 and 3 make 6.

Primary Mathematics (Standards Edition) Extra Practice 1

Exercise 1 : Making Number Stories

1. Draw lines to show the two parts in each set.

(a)

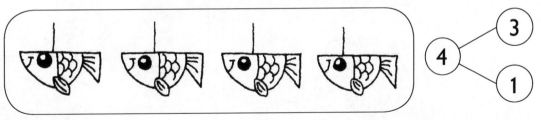

(b)

(c)

2. Draw the missing part.

(a)

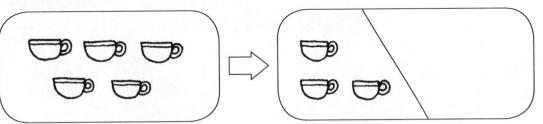

(b)

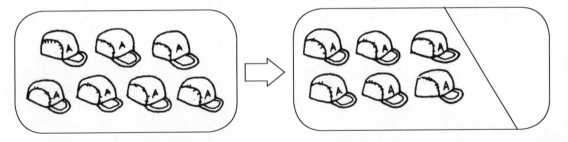

3. Fill in the missing numbers.

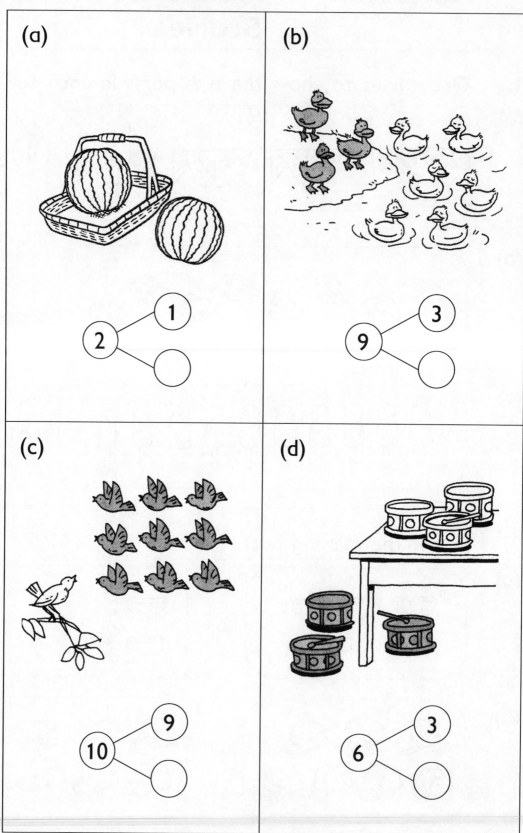

(a)

2 — 1

(b)

9 — 3

(c)

10 — 9

(d)

6 — 3

Primary Mathematics (Standards Edition) Extra Practice 1
© 2008 Marshall Cavendish International (Singapore) Private Limited

4. Write the missing numbers.

(a)

(b)

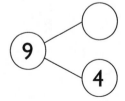

(c)
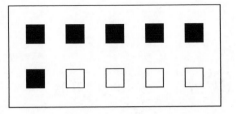

(d)

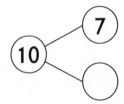

(e)

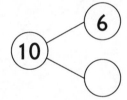

(f)

Primary Mathematics (Standards Edition) Extra Practice 1

5. Write the missing numbers.

(a)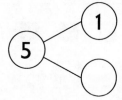

(b)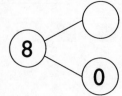

(c)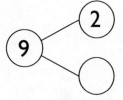

(d)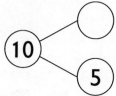

(e)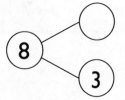

(f)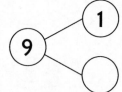

(g)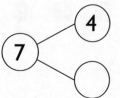

(h)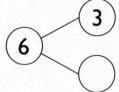

Primary Mathematics (Standards Edition) Extra Practice 1

Unit 3 : Addition

Addition

Addition means **putting together**.

Let us make an addition story.

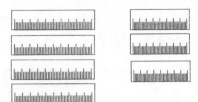

We put together 4 rulers and 3 rulers to get 7 rulers.

There are **4** long rulers.
There are **3** short rulers.
There are **7** rulers altogether.

We can count on to add the number of rulers.

Begin with 4 and count on to 5, 6 and 7.

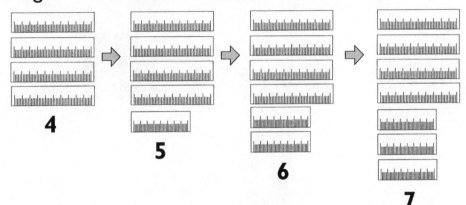

We can use number bonds to show addition.

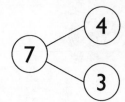 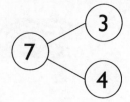

We write the number sentences:

4 + 3 = 7
3 + 4 = 7

Add 4 to 3.
Add 3 to 4.
The answer is 7.

4 + 3 = 7
"Four plus three equals seven."

3 + 4 = 7
"Three plus four equals seven."

'+' means 'add'.
'=' means 'equal'.

Primary Mathematics (Standards Edition) Extra Practice 1

Exercise 1 : Making Addition Stories

1. Fill in the blanks.

(a)

There are _____ black shirts.

There are _____ white shirts.

There are _____ shirts altogether.

(b)

There are _____ small fish.

There are _____ big fish.

There are _____ fish altogether.

(c)

There are _____ men.

There are _____ women.

There are _____ people altogether.

© 2008 Marshall Cavendish International (Singapore) Private Limited

2. Fill in the blanks.

(a)

There are _____ oranges altogether.

(b)

There are _____ cups altogether.

(c)

There are 4 balloons in the sky.

Add _____ more.

There are _____ balloons in all.

(d)

There are 5 robots.

Add _____ more.

There are _____ robots altogether.

Exercise 2 : Addition with Number Bonds

1. Fill in the missing numbers.

(a)

$\boxed{}$ + $\boxed{}$ = 10

(b)

$\boxed{}$ + $\boxed{}$ = 8

(c)

1 + 4 = $\boxed{}$

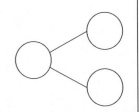

(d)

4 + 2 = $\boxed{}$

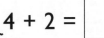

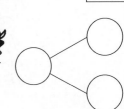

2. Tell a story for each picture.
   Then complete the number sentence.

(a)

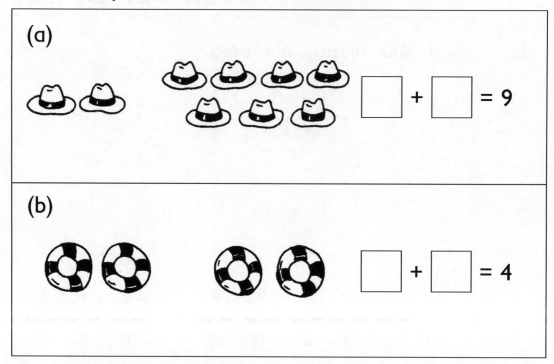

$\boxed{} + \boxed{} = 9$

(b)

$\boxed{} + \boxed{} = 4$

3. Tell two different stories for each picture.
   Then complete the number sentences.

(a)

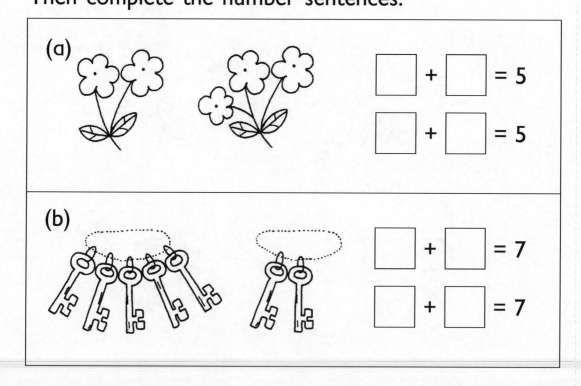

$\boxed{} + \boxed{} = 5$

$\boxed{} + \boxed{} = 5$

(b)

$\boxed{} + \boxed{} = 7$

$\boxed{} + \boxed{} = 7$

Primary Mathematics (Standards Edition) Extra Practice 1

Exercise 3A : Other Methods of Addition

1. Add.

(a)
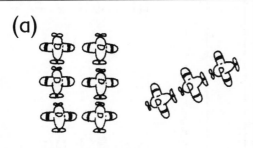
6 + 3 = _____

(b)

3 + 2 = _____

(c)

4 + 2 = _____

(d)

7 + 3 = _____

(e)

5 + 0 = _____

(f)

1 + 1 = _____

(g)
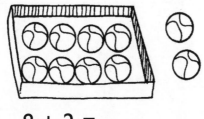
8 + 2 = _____

(h)

5 + 3 = _____

Primary Mathematics (Standards Edition) Extra Practice 1

2.   Add.

(a) 1 + 8 =

(b) 3 + 5 =

(c) 6 + 4 =

(d) 2 + 5 =

(e) 3 + 4 =

(f) 2 + 7 =

(g) 0 + 10 =

(h) 1 + 6 =

(i) 2 + 2 =

(j) 6 + 2 =

(k) 9 + 0 =

(l) 2 + 3 =

(m) 7 + 1 =

(n) 4 + 4 =

(o) 1 + 9 =

(p) 1 + 4 =

Primary Mathematics (Standards Edition) Extra Practice 1

3. Draw and complete the number sentences.

(a)

3 leaves 	Draw 3 more leaves.

3 + 3 = ☐

(b)

4 snails	Draw 1 more snail.

4 + 1 = ☐

4. Fill in the missing numbers.

(a) There are 2 pencils in the pencil case.
Add 8 more.

2 + 8 = ☐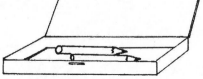

There will be ☐ pencils in the pencil case.

(b) There are 3 toothbrushes in the mug.
Add 6 more.

3 + 6 = ☐

There will be ☐ toothbrushes in the mug.

21

5. Count on to add.

(a)

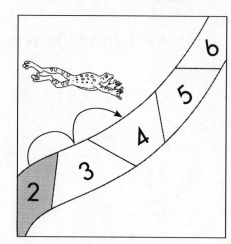

$2 + 2 = $ ☐

(b)

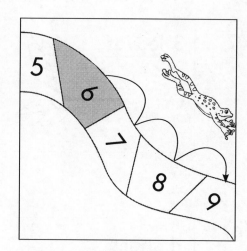

$6 + 3 = $ ☐

6. Do these.

(a) ☐ 5 ——————— + 1 ——————→ ☐

(b) ☐ 6 ——————— + 2 ——————→ ☐

(c) ☐ 4 ——————— + 3 ——————→ ☐

(d) ☐ 2 ——————— + 4 ——————→ ☐

(e) ☐ 5 ——————— + 5 ——————→ ☐

Primary Mathematics (Standards Edition) Extra Practice 1

Exercise 3B : Other Methods of Addition

1. Fill in the missing numbers.

(a)

How many monkeys are there altogether?

$4 + 2 = $ ▢

There are ▢ monkeys altogether.

(b)

How many bicycles are there in all?

$2 + 1 = $ ▢

There are ▢ bicycles in all.

(c)

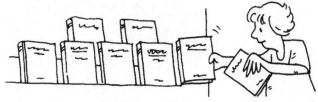

How many books are there altogether?

$6 + 2 = $ ▢

There are ▢ books altogether.

(d)

If I put 4 more stamps in the album, how many stamps will there be in the album?

$5 + 4 = \boxed{}$

There will be $\boxed{}$ stamps in the album.

(e)

If I draw 3 more candles, how many candles will there be on the blackboard?

$7 + 3 = \boxed{}$

There will be $\boxed{}$ candles on the blackboard.

Primary Mathematics (Standards Edition) Extra Practice 1

Exercise 3C : Other Methods of Addition

1. Match.

    7 + 2 •   • 6

    2 + 6 •   • 5

    5 + 1 •   • 9

    3 + 4 •   • 3

    4 + 1 •   • 7

    1 + 2 •   • 8

    8 + 2 •   • 2

    0 + 2 •   • 4

    1 + 3 •   • 10

2. Add.

(a) (5 + 5) = □

(b) (7 + 1) = □

(c) (3 + 5) = □

(d) (6 + 3) = □

(e) (3 + 6) = □

(f) (2 + 8) = □

(g) (1 + 0) = □

(h) (0 + 10) = □

Unit 4 : Subtraction

Friendly Notes

Subtraction

Subtraction means **taking away**.

Let us make a subtraction story.

Cross out 5 cakes.

There are **9** cupcakes.
Jack eats **5** cupcakes.
4 cupcakes are left.

We write the number sentence:

$$9 - 5 = 4$$

Subtract 5 from 9.
The answer is 4.

We say:
"Nine minus five equals four."

'–' means 'subtract'.

27

Methods of Subtraction

We can use number bonds to show subtraction:

9 = 4 + 5
9 – 4 = 5

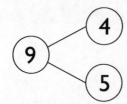

9 = 5 + 4
9 – 5 = 4

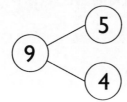

We can count backwards to subtract.

Subtract 4 from 10.
Begin with 10 and count backwards.

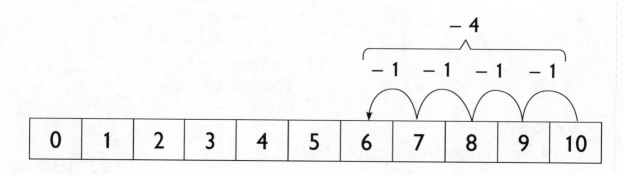

Primary Mathematics (Standards Edition) Extra Practice 1

Exercise 1A : Making Subtraction Stories

1.   Fill in the blanks.

(a)

There are 7 ants.

_____ crawl away.

_____ ants are left.

(b)

There are 5 mangoes.

I take away _____.

_____ mangoes are left.

(c)

There are 4 tricycles.

David rides one tricycle away.

_____ tricycles are left.

(d)

There are 10 animals altogether.

8 of them are birds. The rest are dogs.

There are _____ dogs.

2. Tell a story for each picture.
Then complete the number sentence.

(a)

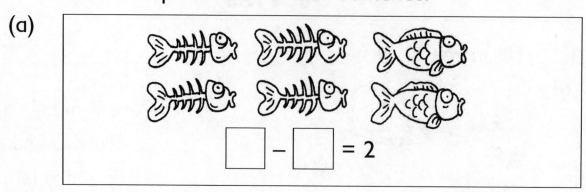

$$\boxed{} - \boxed{} = 2$$

(b)

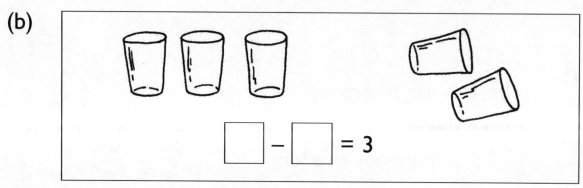

$$\boxed{} - \boxed{} = 3$$

3. Fill in the missing numbers.

(a)

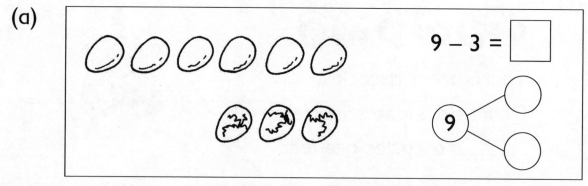

$9 - 3 = \boxed{}$

(b)

$3 - 2 = \boxed{}$

Primary Mathematics (Standards Edition) Extra Practice 1   © 2008 Marshall Cavendish International (Singapore) Private Limited

Exercise 1B : Making Subtraction Stories

1. Fill in the missing numbers.

(a)

How many apples are left?

6 − 1 = ☐

☐ apples are left.

(b)

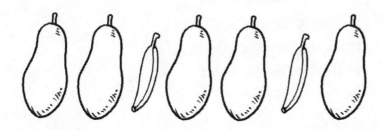

How many fruits are papayas?

7 − 2 = ☐

☐ fruits are papayas.

(c)

There are 8 dogs and cats.

There are 5 dogs.

How many cats are there?

$$8 - 5 = \boxed{}$$

There are $\boxed{}$ cats.

(d)

If I eat 6 cookies, how many cookies will there be left?

$$10 \bigcirc 6 = \boxed{}$$

There will be $\boxed{}$ cookies left.

Primary Mathematics (Standards Edition) Extra Practice 1

(e)

 If I take 7 cookies away, how many cookies will there be left?

8 ◯ 7 = ☐

There will be ☐ cookie left.

(f)

How many birds are left on the branch?

☐ ◯ ☐ = ☐

☐ birds are left on the branch.

(g)

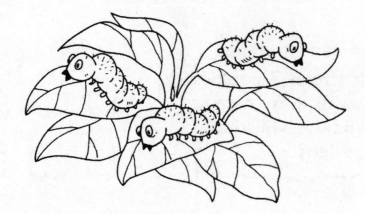

There are 5 caterpillars in all.

How many caterpillars are hidden?

[ ] ◯ [ ] = [ ]

[ ] caterpillars are hidden.

(h)

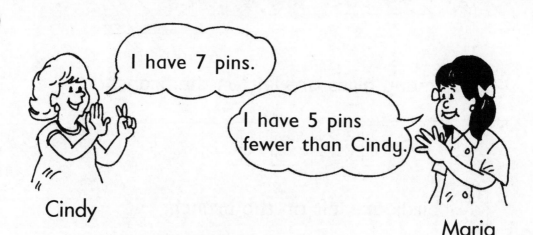

I have 7 pins.

I have 5 pins fewer than Cindy.

Cindy

Maria

How many pins does Maria have?

[ ] ◯ [ ] = [ ]

Maria has [ ] pins.

Exercise 2A : Methods of Subtraction

1. Subtract.

(a)

7 − 2 = _____

(b)

6 − 3 = _____

(c)

4 − 4 = _____

(d)

2 − 1 = _____

(e)

5 − 4 = _____

(f)

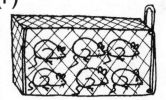

8 − 6 = _____

(g)

9 − 0 = _____

(h)

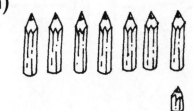

8 − 1 = _____

2. Subtract.

(a) $9 - 3 =$

(b) $4 - 2 =$

(c) $6 - 5 =$

(d) $10 - 7 =$

(e) $3 - 0 =$

(f) $5 - 3 =$

(g) $10 - 8 =$

(h) $1 - 1 =$

(i) $7 - 6 =$

(j) $8 - 2 =$

(k) $5 - 1 =$

(l) $2 - 2 =$

(m) $8 - 5 =$

(n) $9 - 7 =$

(o) $10 - 4 =$

(p) $9 - 3 =$

Primary Mathematics (Standards Edition) Extra Practice 1

Exercise 2B : Methods of Subtraction

1. Write '+' or '−' in each ◯.

(a)

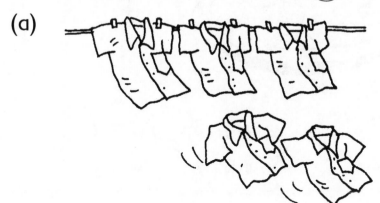

$$5 \bigcirc 2 = 3$$

(b)

$$7 \bigcirc 1 = 8$$

Primary Mathematics (Standards Edition) Extra Practice 1

2. Write '+' or '−' in each .

(a) 4 ◯ 3 = 7

(b) 3 ◯ 4 = 7

(c) 7 ◯ 3 = 4

(d) 7 ◯ 4 = 3

3. Write '+' or '−' in each ◯.

(a) 6 ◯ 4 = 10

(b) 4 ◯ 6 = 10

(c) 10 ◯ 4 = 6

(d) 10 ◯ 6 = 4

Primary Mathematics (Standards Edition) Extra Practice 1   © 2008 Marshall Cavendish International (Singapore) Private Limited

4. Write two addition sentences and two subtraction sentences for the picture.

□ ○ □ = □   □ ○ □ = □

□ ○ □ = □   □ ○ □ = □

---

5. Use the numbers and signs in each box to write a number sentence.

(a) | 3, 5, 2, =, − |

(b) | 4, 10, 6, =, + |

_____   _____

(c) | 1, 6, 7, =, + |

(d) | 0, 8, 8, =, − |

_____   _____

Primary Mathematics (Standards Edition) Extra Practice 1

6. Count backwards to subtract.

(a)

$$8 - 2 = \boxed{}$$

(b)

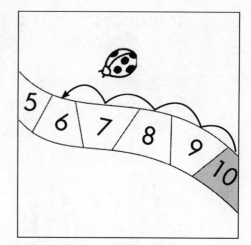

$$10 - 4 = \boxed{}$$

7. Do these.

(a) $\boxed{5} \xrightarrow{\quad -1 \quad} \boxed{}$

(b) $\boxed{7} \xrightarrow{\quad -2 \quad} \boxed{}$

(c) $\boxed{6} \xrightarrow{\quad -3 \quad} \boxed{}$

(d) $\boxed{10} \xrightarrow{\quad -4 \quad} \boxed{}$

(e) $\boxed{1} \xrightarrow{\quad -0 \quad} \boxed{}$

Primary Mathematics (Standards Edition) Extra Practice 1

Exercise 2C : Methods of Subtraction

1. Match.

    $10 - 3$ •   • 3

    $8 - 5$ •   • 4

    $1 - 1$ •   • 7

    $6 - 2$ •   • 9

    $7 - 5$ •   • 5

    $9 - 3$ •   • 6

    $10 - 2$ •   • 0

    $8 - 3$ •   • 8

    $9 - 0$ •   • 2

2. Subtract.

(a) $\boxed{7 - 2}$ = ☐

(b) $\boxed{10 - 6}$ = ☐

(c) $\boxed{6 - 1}$ = ☐

(d) $\boxed{7 - 3}$ = ☐

(e) $\boxed{5 - 1}$ = ☐

(f) $\boxed{9 - 6}$ = ☐

(g) $\boxed{8 - 8}$ = ☐

(h) $\boxed{4 - 2}$ = ☐

Primary Mathematics (Standards Edition) Extra Practice 1

Unit 5 : Position

Position

We use these words to say where things are:

above **below** **next to** **left** **right**

Study this picture.

Left

Right

The birds are flying **above** the clothes line.
The cat is sitting **below** the clothes line.
The skirt is **next to** the overalls.
The T-shirt is also **next to** the overalls.
The dress is on the **left**.
The pair of shorts is on the **right**.

Direction

To give directions, we can also count the number of steps to go **left**, **right** or **up**.

Jane and Jack go shopping.
How do they get to the shops and supermarket?

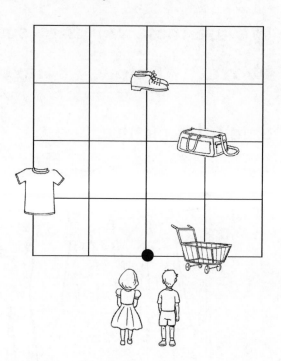

Supermarket:
Turn **right** and go **1 step**.

Clothes shop:
Go **up 1 step**.
Turn **left** and go **2 steps**.

Shoes shop:
Go **up 3 steps**.

Bags shop:
Go **up 2 steps**.
Turn **right** and go **1 step**.

OR

Go **up 1 step**.
Turn **right** and go **1 step**.
Go **up 1 step**.

Primary Mathematics (Standards Edition) Extra Practice 1

© 2008 Marshall Cavendish International (Singapore) Private Limited

Ordinal Numbers – Naming Position

Ordinal numbers help us tell the position of a person or an object.

Cardinal Numbers	Ordinal Numbers
1	1st (first)
2	2nd (second)
3	3rd (third)
4	4th (fourth)
5	5th (fifth)
6	6th (sixth)
7	7th (seventh)
8	8th (eighth)
9	9th (ninth)
10	10th (tenth)

9th is spelt without an 'e': 'ninth', not 'nineth'.

1st 2nd 3rd 4th 5th 6th 7th 8th 9th 10th

When we write ordinal numbers, the last two letters of each word are used. For example: **1st** (fi**rst**), **2nd** (seco**nd**) and **3rd** (thi**rd**), **4th** (four**th**).

Primary Mathematics (Standards Edition) Extra Practice 1

Ordinal numbers can be used to name positions from the left or right.

There are 5 fruits.

papaya   pear   apple   banana   orange

Left   Right

If we count from the left:

The papaya is **1st from the left**.
The pear is **2nd from the left**.
The orange is **5th from the left**.

If we count from the right:

The orange is **1st from the right**.
The banana is **2nd from the right**.
The papaya is **5th from the right**.

The orange is **last from the left**.
The papaya is **last from the right**.

Exercise 1 : Position and Direction

1. Fill in the blanks.

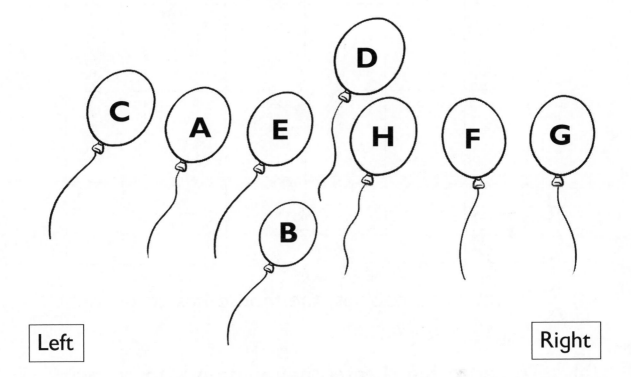

Left

Right

(a) Balloon _____ is below all the other balloons.

(b) Balloon _____ is next to Balloon G.

(c) Balloon _____ is on the far left.

(d) Balloon _____ is above all the other balloons.

2. Fill in the blanks.

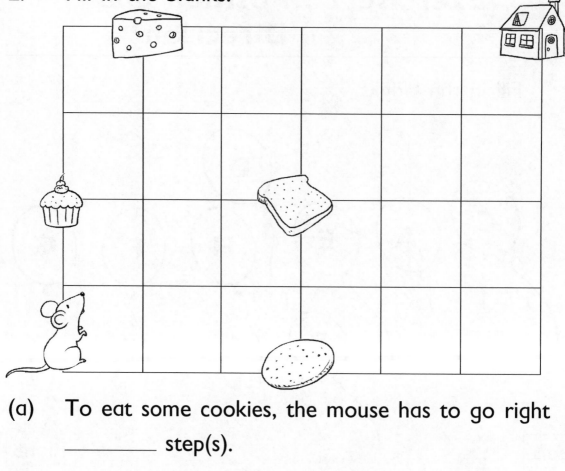

(a) To eat some cookies, the mouse has to go right
 _____ step(s).

(b) To get to the cheese, the mouse has to go right
 _____ step(s) and up _____ step(s).

(c) To find the cupcake, the mouse can go right
 _____ step(s), up _____ step(s) and
 left _____ step(s).

(d) To eat some toast, the mouse has to go up
 _____ step(s) and right _____ step(s).

(e) To go home, the mouse can go right
 _____ step(s) and up _____ steps.

Exercise 2 : Ordinal Numbers – Naming Position

1. Match to show the correct order.

| 2nd | 4th | 1st | 6th | 3rd |

2. Color.

(a) The 2nd jug.

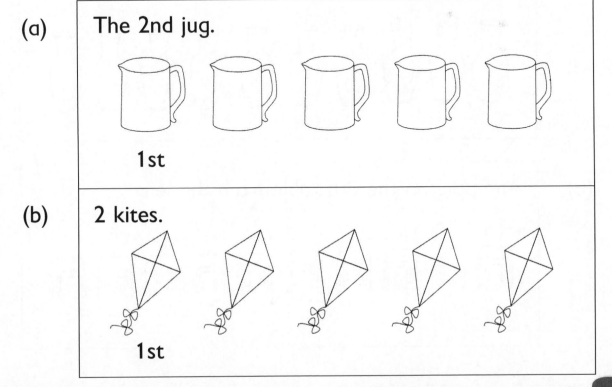

1st

(b) 2 kites.

1st

(c) The 4th book.

1st

(d) 4 rulers.

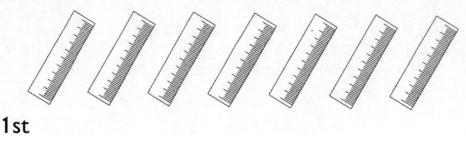

1st

3. Draw.

(a) A flower in the 5th vase from the right.

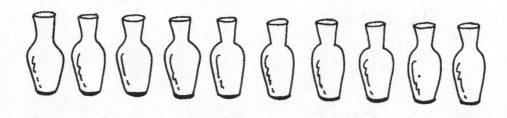

(b) An apple on the 8th table from the left.

Unit 6 : Numbers to 20

Friendly Notes

Counting

These are the numbers 11 to 20.
We learn to count and write these numbers in words.

11 eleven	🐥🐥🐥🐥🐥🐥🐥🐥🐥🐥	🐥
12 twelve	🐥🐥🐥🐥🐥🐥🐥🐥🐥🐥	🐥🐥
13 thirteen	🐥🐥🐥🐥🐥🐥🐥🐥🐥🐥	🐥🐥🐥
14 fourteen	🐥🐥🐥🐥🐥🐥🐥🐥🐥🐥	🐥🐥🐥🐥
15 fifteen	🐥🐥🐥🐥🐥🐥🐥🐥🐥🐥	🐥🐥🐥🐥🐥
16 sixteen	🐥🐥🐥🐥🐥🐥🐥🐥🐥🐥	🐥🐥🐥🐥🐥🐥
17 seventeen	🐥🐥🐥🐥🐥🐥🐥🐥🐥🐥	🐥🐥🐥🐥🐥🐥🐥
18 eighteen	🐥🐥🐥🐥🐥🐥🐥🐥🐥🐥	🐥🐥🐥🐥🐥🐥🐥🐥
19 nineteen	🐥🐥🐥🐥🐥🐥🐥🐥🐥🐥	🐥🐥🐥🐥🐥🐥🐥🐥🐥
20 twenty	🐥🐥🐥🐥🐥🐥🐥🐥🐥🐥	🐥🐥🐥🐥🐥🐥🐥🐥🐥🐥

Primary Mathematics (Standards Edition) Extra Practice 1

To make bigger numbers easier to count, we can make groups of 10 first.

Count the stars.

Count on from 10:
10, 11, 12, ... 18

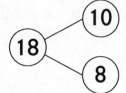

10 and 8 make 18.
10 + 8 = 18

There are 18 stars altogether.

Ordering and Comparing Numbers

When we compare two numbers, we check which number is greater and which is smaller.

Which number is greater? Count and compare.

Set A has 15 bees.

Set B has 12 bees.

There are 3 more bees in Set A than in Set B.
15 is **greater** than 12.
12 is **smaller** than 15.

Primary Mathematics (Standards Edition) Extra Practice 1

When we compare two numbers, we use these words:

greater than   **smaller than**

When we compare more than two numbers, we use these words:

the greatest   **the smallest**

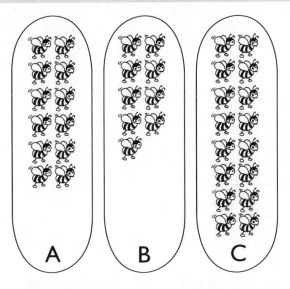

9 is smaller than 12 and 16.
9 is the smallest.
16 is greater than 9 and 12.
16 is the greatest.

Set B has the smallest number.
Set C has the greatest number.

We can arrange numbers in order when we know how to count them in order.

Let us compare these numbers and arrange them in order.

(a)   Begin with the greatest: 13, 10, 8, 4

(b)   Begin with the smallest: 4, 8, 10, 13

Primary Mathematics (Standards Edition) Extra Practice 1

Addition

We can first make 10 to help us add.

Add 8 and 5.

Step 1: Add 8 and 2 to make 10.
Step 2: Add 10 and 3. We get 13.

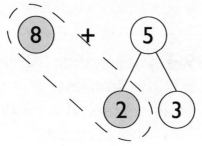 

OR

Step 1: Add 5 and 5 to make 10.
Step 2: Add 10 and 3. We get 13.

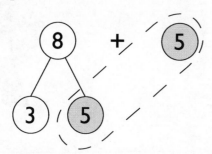 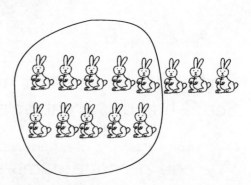

Subtraction

We can first make 10, then subtract.

Subtract 9 from 15.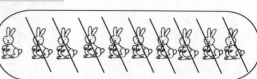

Step 1: We make a 10.
Step 2: Subtract 9 from 10. We get 1.
Step 3: Add 5 and 1. We get 6.

Primary Mathematics (Standards Edition) Extra Practice 1

Exercise 1 : Counting and Comparing

1.   Write the correct number in the boxes.

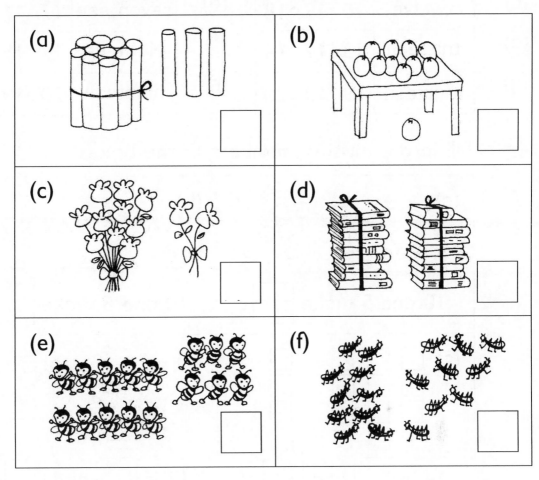

(a)

(b)

(c)

(d)

(e)

(f)

2.   Circle a set of 10 shells. Then write the number.

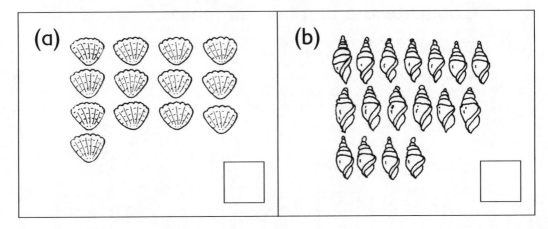

(a)

(b)

3. Circle the correct number.

(a)

eleven	13	15	11

(b)

sixteen	20	16	12

(c)

twelve	20	12	18

(d)

seventeen	17	11	18

(e)

thirteen	13	17	14

(f)

eighteen	16	19	18

(g)

fourteen	19	14	20

(h)

nineteen	20	19	13

4. Fill in the missing numbers in the boxes.

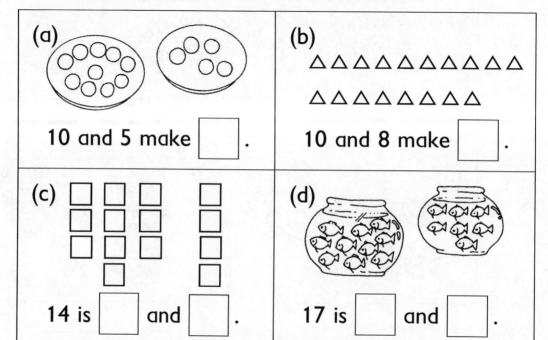

(a) 10 and 5 make ☐.

(b) 10 and 8 make ☐.

(c) 14 is ☐ and ☐.

(d) 17 is ☐ and ☐.

5. Complete the number sentences.

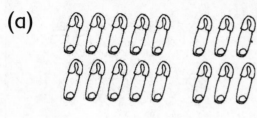

(a) 10 + 6 = ☐

(b) 10 + 9 = ☐

Primary Mathematics (Standards Edition) Extra Practice 1

© 2008 Marshall Cavendish International (Singapore) Private Limited

6. Join the dots in order from 1 to 20.

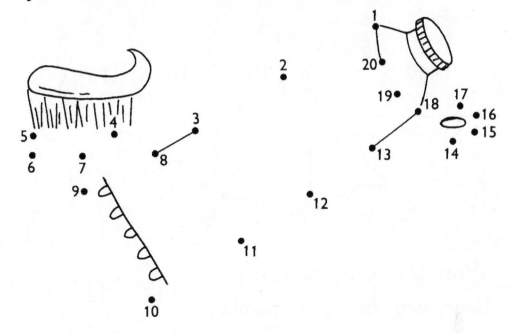

7. Fill in the missing numbers.

(a)
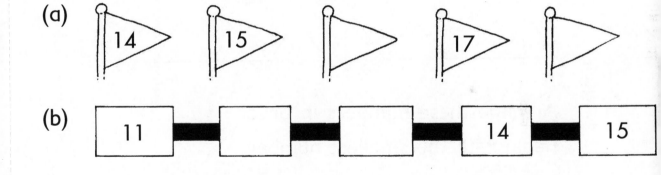

(b)

11			14	15

(c)

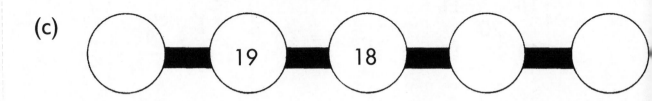

	19	18		

8. Circle the smaller number.

(a) 15   11

(b) 13   20

(c) 17   14

Primary Mathematics (Standards Edition) Extra Practice 1

9.   Color to show the greatest number.

(a)

(b)

10.   Write the numbers in order.
      Begin with the given number.

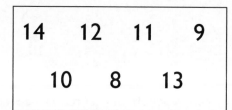

14	12	11	9
	10	8	13

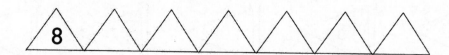

11.   Arrange these numbers in order.
      Begin with the smallest number.

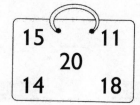   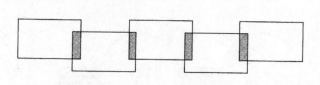

12.   Arrange these numbers in order.
      Begin with the greatest number.

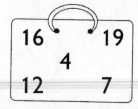

Primary Mathematics (Standards Edition) Extra Practice 1   © 2008 Marshall Cavendish International (Singapore) Private Limited

Exercise 2A : Addition and Subtraction

1.   Add.

(a)

10 + 4 = _____

(b)

10 + 9 = _____

(c)

7 + 10 = _____

(d)

5 + 10 = _____

(e)
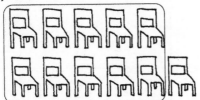

5 + 6 = _____

(f)
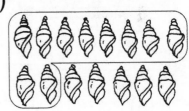

8 + 7 = _____

(g)
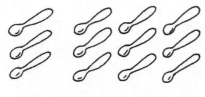

3 + 9 = _____

(h)
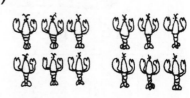

6 + 6 = _____

2. Add.

(a)

12 + 7 = _____

(b)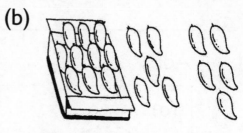

15 + 5 = _____

(c)

6 + 11 = _____

(d)

13 + 3 = _____

(e)

17 + 3 = _____

(f)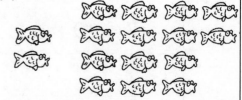

2 + 14 = _____

(g)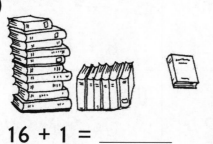

16 + 1 = _____

(h)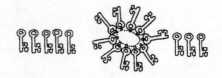

5 + 13 = _____

Exercise 2B : Addition and Subtraction

1. Subtract.

(a)

10 – 6 = _____

(b)

10 – 2 = _____

(c)

14 – 2 = _____

(d)

19 – 9 = _____

(e)

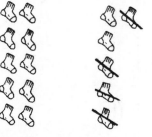

16 – 4 = _____

(f)

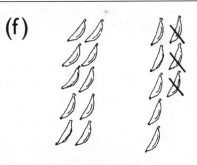

18 – 3 = _____

(g)

14 – 10 = _____

(h)

18 – 10 = _____

2. Subtract.

(a)
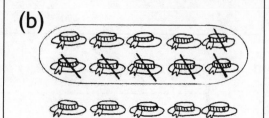
13 − 7 = _____

(b)
15 − 6 = _____

(c)
12 − 9 = _____

(d)
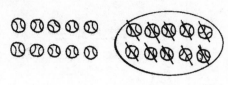
20 − 10 = _____

(e)
16 − 8 = _____

(f)

14 − 7 = _____

(g)
11 − 5 = _____

(h)

17 − 9 = _____

Exercise 2C : Addition and Subtraction

1. Write '+' or '−' in each $\bigcirc$.

(a) $10 \bigcirc 3 = 7$

(b) $16 \bigcirc 10 = 6$

(c) $3 \bigcirc 11 = 14$

(d) $18 \bigcirc 9 = 9$

(e) $13 \bigcirc 5 = 8$

(f) $14 \bigcirc 2 = 16$

(g) $19 \bigcirc 1 = 20$

(h) $17 \bigcirc 9 = 8$

(i) $15 \bigcirc 8 = 7$

(j) $4 \bigcirc 12 = 16$

2. Write a number sentence for each set.

(a) $\boxed{6, 13, 7, -, =}$

(b) $\boxed{20, 10, 10, +, =}$

(c) $\boxed{12, 6, 18, +, =}$

(d) $\boxed{17, 16, 1, -, =}$

© 2008 Marshall Cavendish International (Singapore) Private Limited

Primary Mathematics (Standards Edition) Extra Practice 1

3. Write 4 number sentences for each picture.

(a)

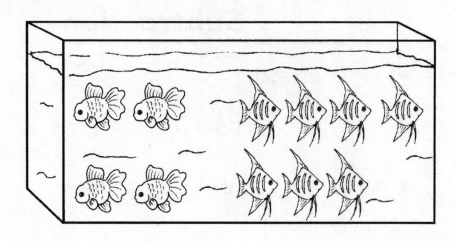

□ ○ □ = □   □ ○ □ = □

□ ○ □ = □   □ ○ □ = □

(b)

□ ○ □ = □   □ ○ □ = □

□ ○ □ = □   □ ○ □ = □

Primary Mathematics (Standards Edition) Extra Practice 1

Exercise 2D : Addition and Subtraction

1.   Add.

(a) $\boxed{8 + 8}$ = $\square$

(b) $\boxed{9 + 9}$ = $\square$

(c) $\boxed{5 + 6}$ = $\square$

(d) $\boxed{6 + 7}$ = $\square$

(e) $\boxed{3 + 8}$ = $\square$

(f) $\boxed{4 + 10}$ = $\square$

2. Match the cards that give the same answers.

7 + 5 •   • 7 + 4

2 + 9 •   • 9 + 4

8 + 7 •   • 6 + 6

7 + 6 •   • 8 + 9

9 + 8 •   • 6 + 9

10 + 8 •   • 9 + 9

9 + 7 •   • 8 + 6

7 + 7 •   • 10 + 6

3.   Match.

$11 - 4$ •   • 11

$19 - 8$ •   • 8

$15 - 9$ •   • 4

$14 - 6$ •   • 6

$12 - 8$ •   • 9

$16 - 7$ •   • 7

$12 - 9$ •   • 10

$17 - 7$ •   • 3

4. Subtract.

(a) $\boxed{18 - 4}$ = $\boxed{}$

(b) $\boxed{19 - 5}$ = $\boxed{}$

(c) $\boxed{11 - 8}$ = $\boxed{}$

(d) $\boxed{13 - 8}$ = $\boxed{}$

(e) $\boxed{17 - 9}$ = $\boxed{}$

(f) $\boxed{15 - 7}$ = $\boxed{}$

(g) $\boxed{12 - 7}$ = $\boxed{}$

(h) $\boxed{14 - 6}$ = $\boxed{}$

Unit 7 : Shapes

Friendly Notes

Common Shapes

These are some common shapes.
These shapes can be used to make new shapes or form pictures.

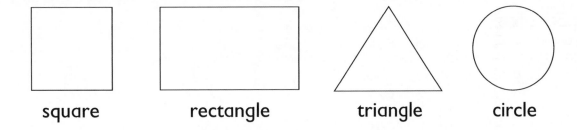

square   rectangle   triangle   circle

Look at these.
What shapes can you see?

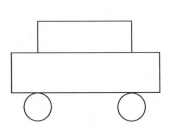

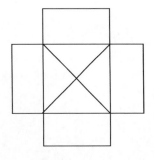

I can see rectangles
and circles.

I can see rectangles,
triangles and a square.

We can group shapes in different ways.

By Shape

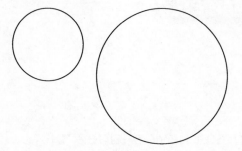 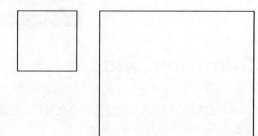

By Size

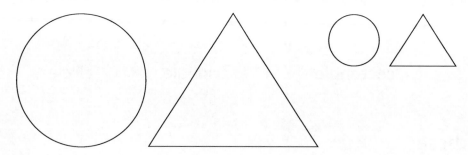

By Color

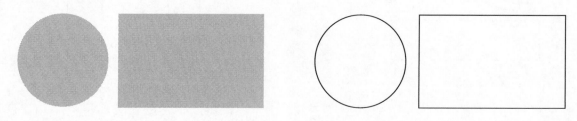

Identifying Patterns

Look at the row of shapes below.
The shapes repeat in a certain way.
They form a pattern.

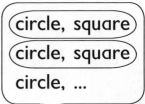

circle, square
circle, square
circle, ...

 ?

The shape that comes next is a square.

Here is another pattern of shapes.
We look at the colors of the shapes.

 ?

The shape that comes next is a gray square.

Here is another pattern of shapes.
We look at the sizes of the shapes.

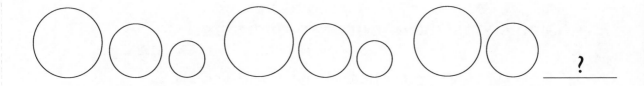 ?

The shape that comes next is the smallest circle.

Some solids have **flat** surfaces.
We can **stack**, **roll** or **slide** objects.

These are flat surfaces.

This is not a flat surface.

I can stack these boxes.

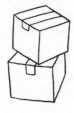

I can roll this marble.

I can slide this ruler.

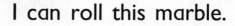

Some shapes have **corners** and **sides**.

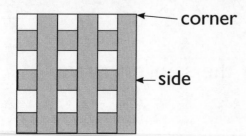

corner

side

Primary Mathematics (Standards Edition) Extra Practice 1   © 2008 Marshall Cavendish International (Singapore) Private Limited

Exercise 1A : Common Shapes

1. Color the shape that matches the object.

(a)

(b)

(c)

(d)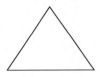

(e)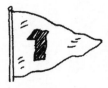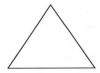

(f)

2. Match the shaded face of each object to the correct shape. Name the shape.

(a) 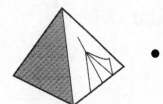 •   •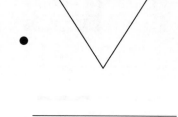
_____

(b)  •   •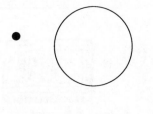
_____

(c)  •   •
_____

(d) 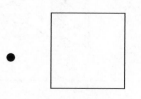 •   •
_____

Primary Mathematics (Standards Edition) Extra Practice 1   © 2008 Marshall Cavendish International (Singapore) Private Limited

3.   Fill in the blanks.

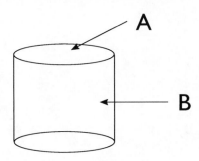

Is A or B a curved surface? _____

4.   Fill in the blanks.

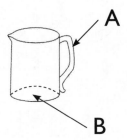

Is A or B a flat surface? _____

5. Check ✔ the correct boxes.

(a) Which objects can we stack?

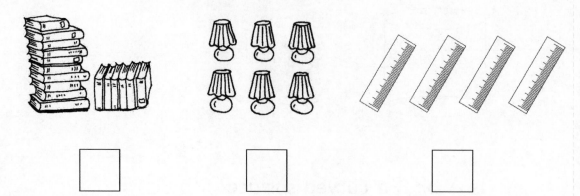

☐   ☐   ☐

(b) Which objects can we roll?

☐   ☐   ☐

(c) Which objects can we slide?

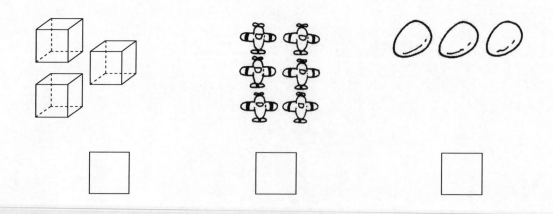

☐   ☐   ☐

Exercise 1B : Common Shapes

1. Draw.

(a) Draw a bigger circle.

(b) Draw a smaller square.

2. Color the train below in this way:

squares – red   rectangles – green

triangles – yellow   circles – black

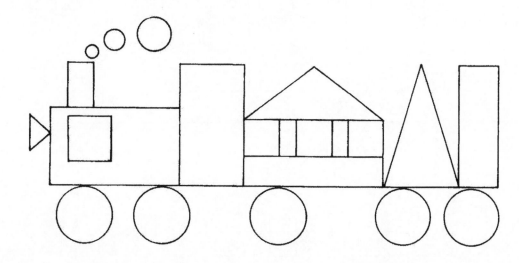

3. Color the shape that comes next.

(a)

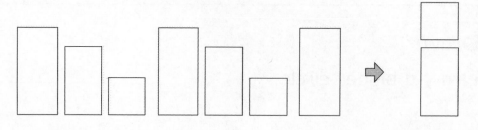

(b)

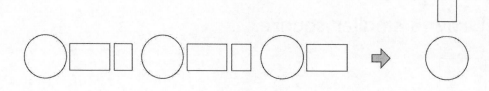

(c)

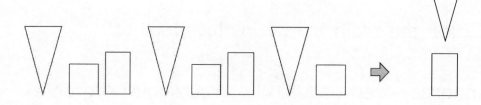

(d)

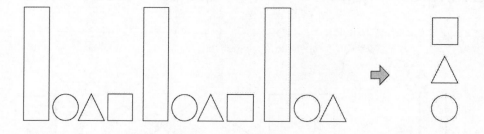

(e)

Unit 8 : Length

Comparing Length

We use these words to compare the lengths of two or more objects.

as long as	**longer than**	**the longest**
as short as	**shorter than**	**the shortest**
as tall as	**taller than**	**the tallest**

Do these pencils have the same length?
Let us compare their lengths.

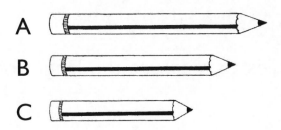

Pencil A is **longer than** Pencil B and Pencil C.
Pencil A is the **longest**.

Pencil C is **shorter than** Pencil A and Pencil B.
Pencil C is the **shortest**.

How tall are the boys? Let us compare how tall they are.

Peter   Chetan   Ming   Reggie

Chetan is **shorter than** Ming.
Ming is **taller than** Chetan.

Ming is **as tall as** Reggie.

Peter is **taller than** Chetan, Ming and Reggie.
Peter is **the tallest** boy.

Chetan is **shorter than** Ming, Reggie and Peter.
Chetan is **the shortest** boy.

Measuring Length

We can use objects to measure length.

We can use paper clips to measure the length of a papaya.
Use ⊂⊃ as 1 unit.

We measure the
papaya this way.

We do not measure the
papaya this way.

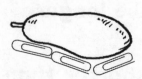

The papaya is about 3 units long.

Exercise 1 : Comparing Length

1. Draw.

(a) Draw a longer pencil.

(b) Draw a shorter string.

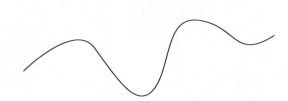

(c) Draw a taller bottle.

(d) Draw a longer ruler.

2.   Color.

(a)   Color the tallest coconut tree.

(b)   Color the shortest flagpole.

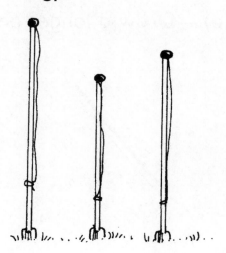

3.   Fill in the blanks.

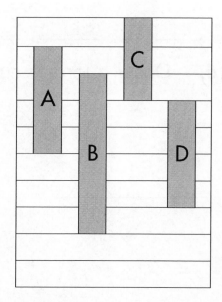

(a)   Tape _____ is the shortest.

(b)   Tape _____ is the longest.

(c)   Tape D is shorter than Tape _____.

(d)   Tape A is as long as Tape _____.

Primary Mathematics (Standards Edition) Extra Practice 1   © 2008 Marshall Cavendish International (Singapore) Private Limited

Exercise 2 : Measuring Length

1. Fill in the blanks.

(a)

The pencil is as long as _____ .

(b)

The chopstick is as long as _____ ⊂━━━━━━━ .

2. Fill in the blanks.

(a) Use ⊂═ as 1 unit.

The length of the duster is about _____ units.

(b) Use 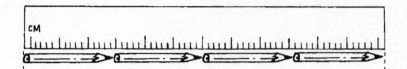 as 1 unit.

The length of the ruler is about _____ units.

(c) Use ⟨pencil⟩ as 1 unit.

The length of the rod is about _____ units.

3. Fill in the blanks.

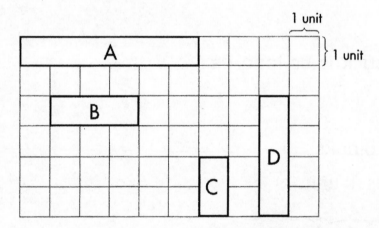

(a) Rectangle A is _____ units long.

(b) Rectangle B is _____ units long.

(c) Rectangle C is _____ units long.

(d) Rectangle D is _____ units long.

Unit 9 : Weight

Friendly Notes

Comparing Weight

We use these words to compare the weight of two or more objects.

as light as	**lighter than**	**the lightest**
as heavy as	**heavier than**	**the heaviest**

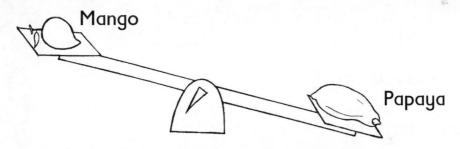

This mango **weighs less** than the papaya.

This mango is **lighter than** the papaya.

This papaya **weighs more** than the mango.

This papaya is **heavier than** the mango.

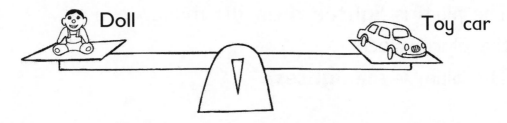

The doll and the toy car have the **same weight**.

The doll is **as heavy as** the toy car.

The toy car is **as light as** the doll.

Primary Mathematics (Standards Edition) Extra Practice 1

Measuring Weight

We can use objects to measure weight.

We can use blocks to measure the weight of the mango, alarm clock and plum. Use ☐ as 1 unit.

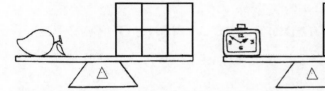

The mango is as heavy as 6 ☐ .
The alarm clock is as heavy as 4 ☐ .
The plum is as heavy as 1 ☐ .

Each ☐ stands for 1 unit.

We can say that:

The mango weighs **6** units.
The alarm clock weighs **4** units.
The plum weighs **1** unit.

The plum is **lighter than** the mango and the alarm clock.
The plum is the **lightest**.

The mango is **heavier than** the alarm clock and the plum.
The mango is the **heaviest**.

Primary Mathematics (Standards Edition) Extra Practice 1

Exercise 1 : Comparing Weight

1. Write 'heavier than', 'lighter than' or 'as heavy as'.

(a)

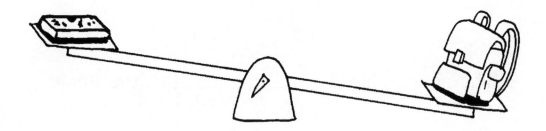

The pencil box is _____ the school bag.

(b)

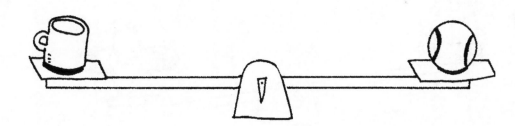

The mug is _____ the ball.

(c)

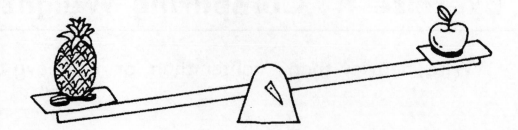

The pineapple is _____ the apple.

(d)

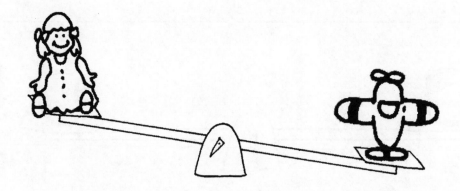

The doll is _____ the toy aeroplane.

Exercise 2 : Measuring Weight

1.   Fill in the blanks. Use  as 1 unit.

(a)   Bottle A weighs _____ units.

(b)   Bottle B weighs _____ units.

(c)   Bottle _____ is the lightest.

(d)   Bottle _____ is the heaviest.

(e)   Bottle A is lighter than Bottle _____ .

2. Fill in the blanks. Use ○ as 1 unit.

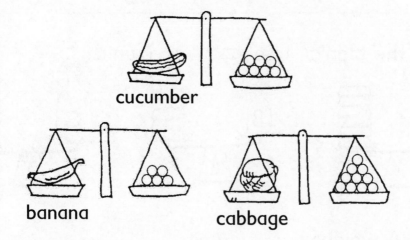

cucumber

banana   cabbage

(a) The banana weighs _____ units.

(b) The cabbage weighs _____ units.

(c) The cucumber is heavier than the _____ .

(d) The _____ is the lightest.

(e) The _____ is the heaviest.

Primary Mathematics (Standards Edition) Extra Practice 1   © 2008 Marshall Cavendish International (Singapore) Private Limited

Unit 10 : Capacity

Friendly Notes

Comparing Capacity

Capacity is the amount a container holds when full.

These bottles are of different size.
They do not hold the same amount of water when full.
They do not have the same capacity.

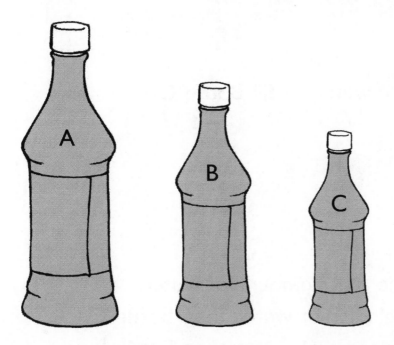

Bottle A holds more water than Bottle B or Bottle C.
Bottle A holds the most amount of water.

Bottle C holds less water than Bottle A or Bottle B.
Bottle C holds the least amount of water.

Measuring Capacity

It takes 6 glasses of water to fill Bottle A.

It takes 3 glasses of water to fill Bottle B.

It takes 1 glass of water to fill Bottle C.

Bottle A holds the most amount of water.
It holds 5 more glasses of water than Bottle C.
It holds 3 more glasses of water than Bottle B.

Bottle C holds the least amount of water.
It holds 5 fewer glasses of water than Bottle A.
It holds 2 fewer glasses of water than Bottle B.

Primary Mathematics (Standards Edition) Extra Practice 1   © 2008 Marshall Cavendish International (Singapore) Private Limited

Exercise 1 : Comparing Capacity

1. Circle the container that can hold the most water.

2. Circle the container that can hold the least water.

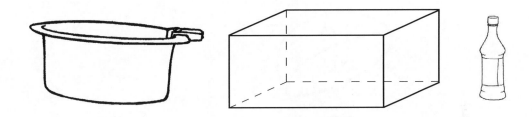

3. Circle the correct answer.

(a) Is there enough water in a tablespoon to fill an empty glass? (Yes, No)

(b) Is there enough water in a full kettle to make one cup of tea? (Yes, No)

(c) Is there enough water in a swimming pool to fill a fish tank? (Yes, No)

(d) Is there enough water in a small water bottle to give a dog a bath? (Yes, No)

4. Which container can hold more water?
Container _____

Primary Mathematics (Standards Edition) Extra Practice 1   © 2008 Marshall Cavendish International (Singapore) Private Limited

Exercise 2 : Measuring Capacity

1.   Fill in the blanks

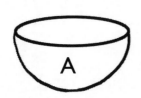

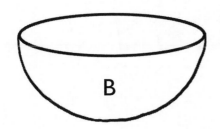
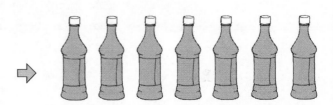

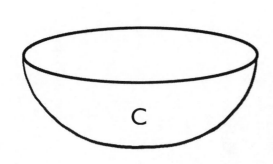
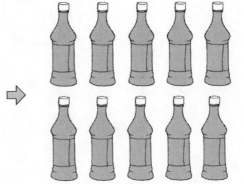

(a)   Which container holds the most water?

Container _____

(b)   Container B holds _____ more bottles of water than

Container A.

(c)   Container A holds _____ fewer bottles of water

than Container C.

Primary Mathematics (Standards Edition) Extra Practice 1

2. **Fill in the blanks.**

    Which pot can hold more water?

(a) Pot _____ can hold more water than Pot _____.

(b) Pot _____ can hold _____ more glasses of water than Pot _____.

Unit 11 : Comparing Numbers

Friendly Notes

More or Less

We can compare numbers by counting, matching or subtracting.

There are **more** bees than flowers.
There are **fewer** flowers than bees.

How many more bees than flowers are there?
Let us subtract to find the answer.

There are 7 bees.
There are 5 flowers.

7 − 5 = 2

7 is 2 more than 5.
5 is 2 less than 7.

There are **2 more** bees than flowers.
There are **2 fewer** flowers than bees.

97

We see that:

2 more than 5 is 7.
5 + 2 = 7

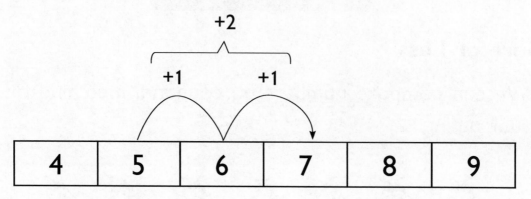

2 less than 7 is 5.
7 − 2 = 5

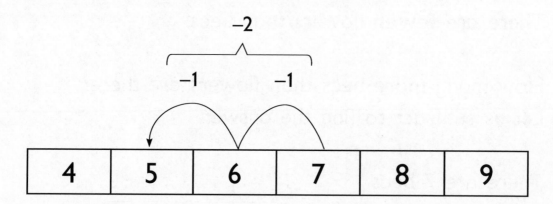

Exercise 1A : Comparing Numbers

1. Write 'Yes' or 'No' in the boxes.

(a)

There are more vases than flowers. ☐

(b)

There are more cats than rats. ☐

(c)

There are more boys than balls. ☐

(d)

There are more saucers than cups. ☐

Primary Mathematics (Standards Edition) Extra Practice 1

2. Draw.

(a)

Draw 1 more apple.

1 more than 6 is _____.

(b)

Draw 1 more star.

1 more than 3 is _____.

3. Cross.

(a)

Cross out 1 fish.

1 less than 10 is _____.

(b)

Cross out 1 crab.

1 less than 6 is _____.

Primary Mathematics (Standards Edition) Extra Practice 1   © 2008 Marshall Cavendish International (Singapore) Private Limited

Exercise 1B : Comparing Numbers

1. Join each balloon to the correct answer on the number line.

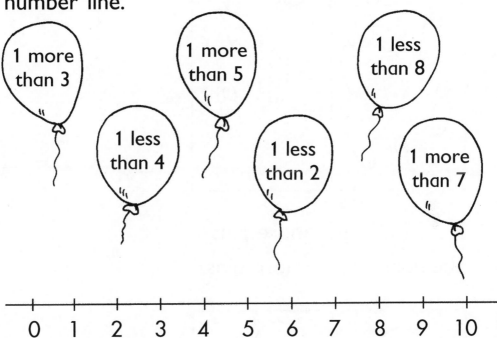

2. Fill in the blanks.

(a)

There are _____ more fish than cats.

(b)

There are _____ more boys than bicycles.

Primary Mathematics (Standards Edition) Extra Practice 1

3. Fill in the blanks.

(a)

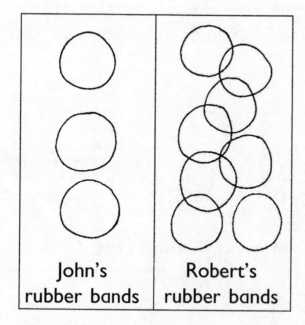

Paula's pins	Siti's pins

_____ has more pins.

She has _____ more pins.

(b)

John's rubber bands	Robert's rubber bands

_____ has more rubber bands.

He has _____ more rubber bands.

Exercise 2 : Comparison by Subtraction

1.   Do these.

(a)   How many more papayas than bananas are there?

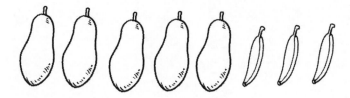

5 − 3 = ☐

There are ☐ more papayas than bananas.

(b)

8 − 5 = ☐

There are ☐ fewer flowers than girls.

(c)

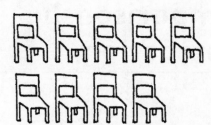 

$9 - 3 = $ ☐

There are ☐ more chairs than tables.

There are ☐ fewer tables than chairs.

Primary Mathematics (Standards Edition) Extra Practice 1
© 2008 Marshall Cavendish International (Singapore) Private Limited

Unit 12 : Graphs

Picture Graphs

We can use picture graphs to compare the number of items.

Caleb has 7 carrots.
Daniel has 2 carrots.
Emily has 4 carrots.

This is how our picture graph may look:

Caleb	🥕 🥕 🥕 🥕 🥕 🥕 🥕
Daniel	🥕 🥕
Emily	🥕 🥕 🥕 🥕

or ...

... our picture graph may also look like this:

Number of Carrots Each Child Has		
Caleb	Daniel	Emily

From the picture graph, we can tell:

Caleb has **5** more carrots than Daniel.

Daniel has **2** fewer carrots than Emily.

Emily has **3** fewer carrots than Caleb.

Caleb, Daniel and Emily have 13 carrots altogether.

Caleb has **more** carrots than Daniel and Emily.

Caleb has the **most** carrots.

Daniel has **fewer** carrots than Caleb and Emily.

Daniel has the **least** carrots.

Primary Mathematics (Standards Edition) Extra Practice 1

© 2008 Marshall Cavendish International (Singapore) Private Limited

Tally Charts

We can also use a tally chart to show how many carrots Caleb, Daniel and Emily have.

This is how our tally chart may look:

	Number of Carrots Each Child Has
Caleb	////// //
Daniel	//
Emily	/////

Each / stands for 1 carrot.

///// is a group of 5.

It stands for 5 carrots.

Bar Graphs

We can also use a bar graph to show the number of carrots each child has.

This is how our bar graph may look:

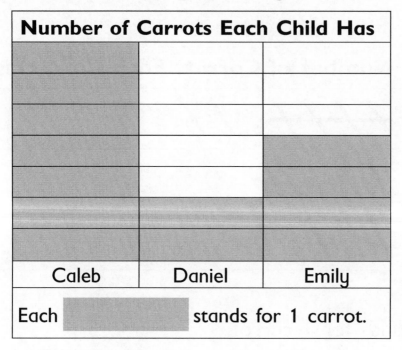

or our bar graph may look like this:

From our bar graph, we can easily tell who has the most number of carrots or the least number of carrots.

Exercise 1A : Graphs

1.

At a Parking Lot		
cars	trucks	scooters

(a) There are _____ scooters.

(b) There are 5 _____ .

(c) There are _____ more scooters than cars.

(d) There are _____ fewer trucks than cars.

2.

Our Books		
Wendy's books	Larry's books	Tyrone's books

(a) Larry has _____ books.

(b) _____ has 6 books.

(c) _____ has the least number of books.

(d) They have _____ books altogether.

3.

Fruits in a Basket

pear	apple	banana
★ ★ ★ ★ ★ ★	★ ★ ★ ★ ★ ★ ★	★ ★ ★

Each ★ stands for 1 fruit.

(a) There are _____ fruits altogether.

(b) The number of _____ is the greatest.

(c) There are _____ fewer bananas than pears.

(d) There are _____ pears.

4.

Toys We Like Best

robot	drum	toy car	doll

Each ▨ stands for 1 child.

(a) There are _____ children who like drums best.

(b) There are _____ more children who like robots than dolls.

(c) Drums are as popular as _____.

(d) The most popular toy is the _____.

(e) The least popular toy is the _____.

Exercise 1B : Graphs

1.   Fill in the blanks.

Colors of Flowers	Number of Flowers	Total
Red	////	
White	/////	
Yellow	/////	

(a)   There are _____ red flowers.

(b)   There are _____ white flowers.

(c)   There are _____ yellow flowers.

(d)   There are _____ flowers altogether.

2.   Make a tally chart.

Type of Fruit	Number of Fruit	Total
Bananas		8
Oranges		5
Pears		9
Apples		4

Circle the correct answer.

(a)   Which fruit has the most tally marks?

       (Apples, Bananas, Oranges, Pears)

(b)   Are there more bananas than any other type of fruit?

       (Yes, No)

3.   Color the correct number of boxes to show

(a)   4 white shirts.

(b)   3 black shirts.

(c)   5 red shirts.

(d)   2 green shirts.

White shirts					
Black shirts					
Red shirts					
Green shirts					

4.   Circle the correct answer.

What kind of graph did you just make?

(Picture graph, Bar graph, Tally chart)

Primary Mathematics (Standards Edition) Extra Practice 1

© 2008 Marshall Cavendish International (Singapore) Private Limited

5. This graph shows what a group of children have for snacks.

Carrots	Cookies	Apples

Each ▭ stands for 1 child.

(a) How many children have cookies for snacks? _____

(b) What snack is the most popular? _____

(c) How many fewer children have carrots than cookies for snacks? _____

6. Use the information shown in the bar graph to make a tally chart.

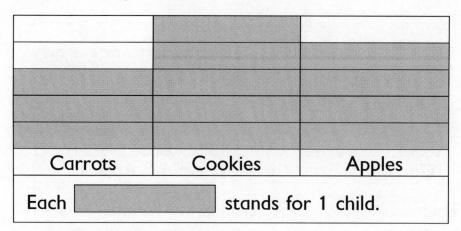

	Carrots	Cookies	Apples

Each [   ] stands for 1 child.

	Number of Children
Carrots	
Cookies	
Apples	

Primary Mathematics (Standards Edition) Extra Practice 1

Unit 13 : Numbers to 40

Friendly Notes

Counting

These are numbers 21 to 40.
We learn to count and write these numbers in words.

Number	Number in Words
21	twenty-one
22	twenty-two
23	twenty-three
24	twenty-four
25	twenty-five
26	twenty-six
27	twenty-seven
28	twenty-eight
29	twenty-nine
30	thirty

Number	Number in Words
31	thirty-one
32	thirty-two
33	thirty-three
34	thirty-four
35	thirty-five
36	thirty-six
37	thirty-seven
38	thirty-eight
39	thirty-nine
40	forty

We write 40 in words
without the 'u': forty.

Primary Mathematics (Standards Edition) Extra Practice 1

To count numbers more than 10, we can make groups of 10 first.

How many butterflies are there?

10, 20, 21, 22, 23, 24, 25, 26, 27, 28, 29.

There are 29 butterflies.

Primary Mathematics (Standards Edition) Extra Practice 1

Tens and Ones

We can count and write numbers in tens and ones.
This makes it easier to compare numbers greater than 10.

(a) Which is smaller, 24 or 20?

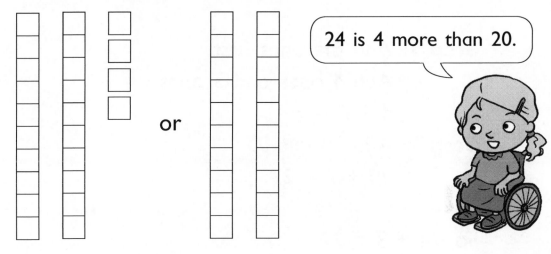

24 is 4 more than 20.

24 = 2 tens 4 ones
20 = 2 tens
20 is smaller.

(b) Circle the smallest number.
Underline the greatest number.

15 is 1 ten and 5 ones.
20 is 2 tens.
24 is 2 tens and 4 ones.
37 is 3 tens and 7 ones.

1 ten is the smallest.
15 is the smallest number.
3 tens is the greatest.
37 is the greatest number.

Primary Mathematics (Standards Edition) Extra Practice 1

Addition Within 40

(a) 24 + 3 = ?

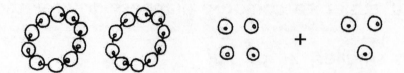

Step 1: Add the ones first.
Add 4 ones and 3 ones.
4 + 3 = 7

Step 2: Add 20 and 7.
20 + 7 = 27

So, 24 + 3 = 27.

To add bigger numbers, we can make a 10 first.

(b) 27 + 5 = ?

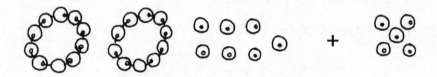

Step 1: Add 27 and 3.
27 + 3 = 30

Step 2: Add 30 and 2.
30 + 2 = 32

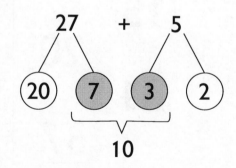

So, 27 + 5 = 32.

Primary Mathematics (Standards Edition) Extra Practice 1

Subtraction Within 40

(a) 36 – 4 = ?

We subtract the ones.

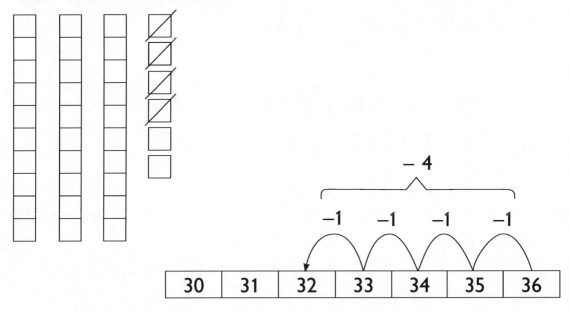

(b) 36 – 8 = ?

We cannot take away 8 ones from 6 ones.
So, we take away from the tens.

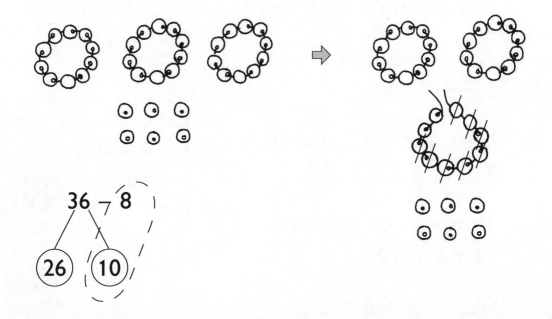

Primary Mathematics (Standards Edition) Extra Practice 1

Adding Three Numbers

There are different ways to add three or more numbers.

(a) 4 + 5 + 1 = ?

Add 4 ones and 5 ones.

4 + 5 = 9

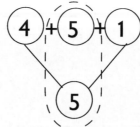

Then we add 9 and 1.

9 + 1 = 10

So, 4 + 5 + 1 = 10.

OR

4 + 1 = 5

5 + 5 = 10

4 + 5 + 1 = 10

(b) 7 + 5 + 8 = ?

We can make a 10 first.

Add 5 ones and 5 ones.

5 + 5 = 10

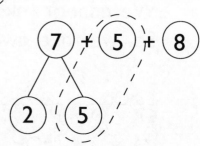

Next, we add 2 and 10.

2 + 10 = 12

We can add in any order:

7 + 5 + 8 = 20

8 + 5 + 7 = 20

5 + 7 + 8 = 20

Then we add 12 and 8.

12 + 8 = 20

So, 7 + 5 + 8 = 20.

Primary Mathematics (Standards Edition) Extra Practice 1   © 2008 Marshall Cavendish International (Singapore) Private Limited

Counting by 2's

This is how we count by 1's.

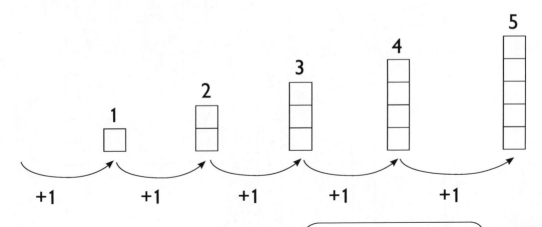

0, 1, 2, 3, 4, 5, ...

$0 + 1 = 1$
$1 + 1 = 2$
$2 + 1 = 3$
$3 + 1 = 4$
$4 + 1 = 5$

OR

$0 + 1 = 1$
$1 + 1 = 2$
$1 + 1 + 1 = 3$
$1 + 1 + 1 + 1 = 4$
$1 + 1 + 1 + 1 + 1 = 5$

This is how we count by 2's.

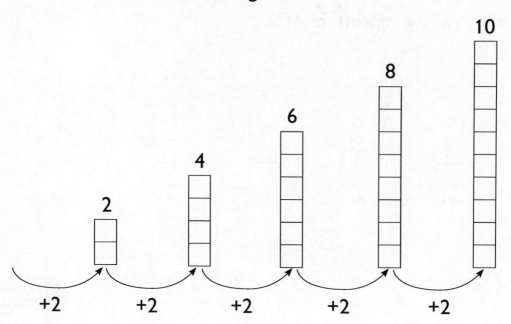

$$0 + 2 = 2$$
$$2 + 2 = 4$$
$$4 + 2 = 6 \quad \text{OR}$$
$$6 + 2 = 8$$
$$8 + 2 = 10$$

$$0 + 2 = 2$$
$$2 + 2 = 4$$
$$2 + 2 + 2 = 6$$
$$2 + 2 + 2 + 2 = 8$$
$$2 + 2 + 2 + 2 + 2 = 10$$

0, 2, 4, 6, 8, 10, ...

Primary Mathematics (Standards Edition) Extra Practice 1
© 2008 Marshall Cavendish International (Singapore) Private Limited

Exercise 1A : Counting

1. Circle groups of 10.

    Then count and write the number in the boxes.

(a)

(b)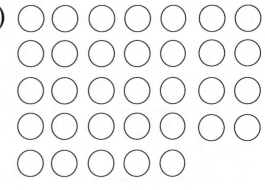

2. Match the numbers to the words.

| 39 | 28 | 20 | 36 |

•   •   •   •

•   •   •   •

| twenty-eight | twenty | thirty-six | thirty-nine |

3. Write the numbers.

(a)
twenty-three

(b)
thirty-five

(c)
twenty-nine

(d)
thirty-one

(e)
thirty-seven

(f)
forty

(g)
twenty-six

(h)
thirty-four

4. Fill in the missing numbers.

(a)

23 24 25   27   29

(b)

40 39   37 36   33

Exercise 1B : Counting

1. Fill in the blanks.

(a)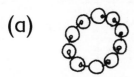

4 more than 20 is _____ .

(b)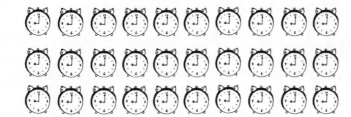

2 more than 30 is _____ .

2. Fill in the missing numbers in the number bonds.

(a)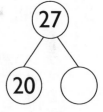

(b)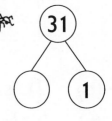

(c)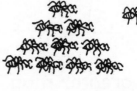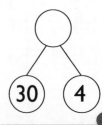

© 2008 Marshall Cavendish International (Singapore) Private Limited

Primary Mathematics (Standards Edition) Extra Practice 1

3. Fill in the missing numbers.

1	2			5	6		8		10
11		13			16			19	
21		24			27				30
	32			35		37			40

4. Fill in the blanks.

(a) 1 more than 26 is _____ .

(b) 1 less than 30 is _____ .

(c) 2 more than 18 is _____ .

(d) 2 less than 35 is _____ .

5. Fill in the blanks.

21   33   18   37

(a) 21 is greater than _____ .

(b) 33 is smaller than _____ .

(c) The greatest number is _____ .

(d) The smallest number is _____ .

Primary Mathematics (Standards Edition) Extra Practice 1

Exercise 2 : Tens and Ones

1. Fill in the blanks.

(a)

27 = _____ tens

_____ ones

(b)

34 = _____ tens

_____ ones

2. Write how many tens and ones.

Then write the number in the box.

(a)

Tens	Ones

 ⟹

(b)

Tens	Ones

 ⟹

Primary Mathematics (Standards Edition) Extra Practice 1

(c)

Tens	Ones

$\Rightarrow$ [   ] ¢

3. Fill in the blanks.

(a)

△△△△△△△△△△
△△△△△△△△△
△△△△△△△△

1 more than 29

is _____ .

10 more than 29

is _____ .

(b)

☆☆☆☆☆☆☆☆☆
☆☆☆☆☆☆☆☆
☆☆☆☆☆☆☆☆

1 less than 24

is _____ .

10 less than 24

is _____ .

(c)

1 more than 32

is _____ .

10 more than 32

is _____ .

(d)

1 less than 35

is _____ .

10 less than 35

is _____ .

Primary Mathematics (Standards Edition) Extra Practice 1

Exercise 3A : Addition and Subtraction

1. Fill in the blanks.

(a)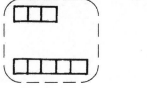

23 + 5 = _____

(b) △△△△△△△△△△
△△△△△△△△△△
△△△△△△△△△△
△△△△△
△

35 + 1 = _____

(c)

24 + 6 = _____

(d)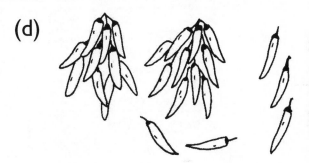

22 + 3 = _____

(e)

37 + 2 = _____

(f)

32 + 4 = _____

Primary Mathematics (Standards Edition) Extra Practice 1

(g)

13 + 8 = _____

(h)

26 + 6 = _____

(i)

27 + 8 = _____

(j)

29 + 5 = _____

(k)

16 + 9 = _____

(l)

25 + 6 = _____

2. Add.

(a)

$4 + 1 = \rule{2cm}{0.4pt}$

$14 + 1 = \rule{2cm}{0.4pt}$

(b)

$2 + 2 = \rule{2cm}{0.4pt}$

$12 + 2 = \rule{2cm}{0.4pt}$

(c)

$6 + 3 = \rule{2cm}{0.4pt}$

$26 + 3 = \rule{2cm}{0.4pt}$

(d)

$5 + 4 = \rule{2cm}{0.4pt}$

$25 + 4 = \rule{2cm}{0.4pt}$

(e)

$3 + 5 = \rule{2cm}{0.4pt}$

$33 + 5 = \rule{2cm}{0.4pt}$

(f)

$2 + 6 = \rule{2cm}{0.4pt}$

$32 + 6 = \rule{2cm}{0.4pt}$

(g)

9 + 3 = _____

19 + 3 = _____

(h)

7 + 6 = _____

27 + 6 = _____

(i)

8 + 4 = _____

18 + 4 = _____

(j)

8 + 7 = _____

28 + 7 = _____

(k)

9 + 5 = _____

29 + 5 = _____

(l)

4 + 6 = _____

34 + 6 = _____

Exercise 3B : Addition and Subtraction

1. Fill in the blanks.

(a)

20 – 8 = _____

(b)

30 – 2 = _____

(c)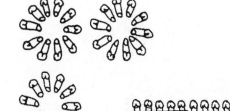

40 – 5 = _____

(d)

30 – 7 = _____

(e)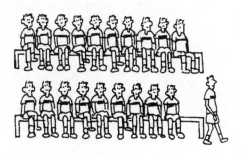

20 – 1 = _____

(f)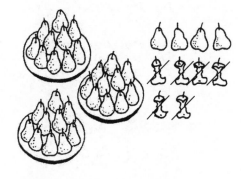

40 – 6 = _____

(g)

$$40 - 1 = \rule{2cm}{0.4pt}$$

(h)

$$30 - 4 = \rule{2cm}{0.4pt}$$

(i)

$$20 - 3 = \rule{2cm}{0.4pt}$$

(j)

$$20 - 5 = \rule{2cm}{0.4pt}$$

(k)

$$30 - 9 = \rule{2cm}{0.4pt}$$

(l)

$$40 - 2 = \rule{2cm}{0.4pt}$$

Primary Mathematics (Standards Edition) Extra Practice 1

2. Subtract.

(a) $2 - 1 =$ _____ $22 - 1 =$ _____	(b) $5 - 2 =$ _____ $25 - 2 =$ _____
(c) $4 - 3 =$ _____ $34 - 3 =$ _____	(d) $8 - 4 =$ _____ $38 - 4 =$ _____
(e) $7 - 5 =$ _____ $37 - 5 =$ _____	(f) $9 - 6 =$ _____ $29 - 6 =$ _____
(g) $11 - 4 =$ _____ $21 - 4 =$ _____	(h) $13 - 6 =$ _____ $23 - 6 =$ _____
(i) $14 - 5 =$ _____ $34 - 5 =$ _____	(j) $15 - 7 =$ _____ $35 - 7 =$ _____
(k) $16 - 9 =$ _____ $26 - 9 =$ _____	(l) $17 - 8 =$ _____ $37 - 8 =$ _____

Primary Mathematics (Standards Edition) Extra Practice 1

3. Add or subtract. Then match the answers.

(a) 5 + 4 = •   • 40 − 20 =

(b) 4 + 10 = •   • 35 − 4 =

(c) 12 + 8 = •   • 20 − 4 =

(d) 2 + 14 = •   • 23 − 9 =

(e) 26 + 5 = •   • 19 − 10 =

(f) 13 + 20 = •   • 36 − 3 =

(g) 17 + 8 = •   • 27 − 1 =

(h) 3 + 12 = •   • 23 − 8 =

(i) 10 + 16 = •   • 40 − 0 =

(j) 39 + 1 = •   • 35 − 10 =

Primary Mathematics (Standards Edition) Extra Practice 1

Exercise 4 : Adding Three Numbers

1. Add.

(a)

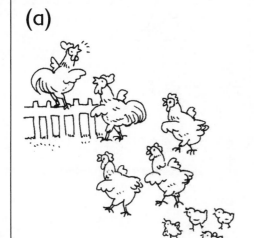

$2 + 3 + 4 = \boxed{}$

(b)

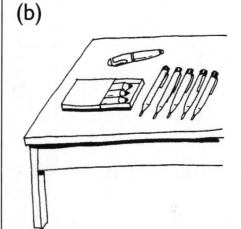

$3 + 5 + 1 = \boxed{}$

(c)

$4 + 8 + 3 = \boxed{}$

(d)

$9 + 6 + 5 = \boxed{}$

2. Add and write the answers in the circles.

(a)

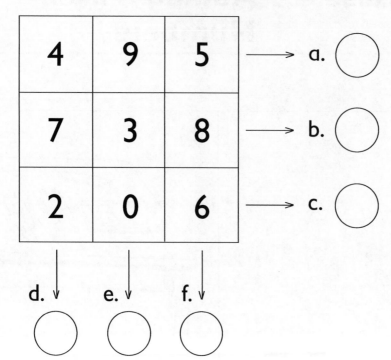

4	9	5	→ a. ◯
7	3	8	→ b. ◯
2	0	6	→ c. ◯

d. ↓   e. ↓   f. ↓
◯   ◯   ◯

(b)

5	6	9	→ a. ◯
1	2	7	→ b. ◯
8	4	3	→ c. ◯

d. ↓   e. ↓   f. ↓
◯   ◯   ◯

Primary Mathematics (Standards Edition) Extra Practice 1

Exercise 5 : Counting by 2's

1. Count by 2's and circle the numbers as you count.

1	2	3	4	5	6	7	8	9	10
11	12	13	14	15	16	17	18	19	20

2. Fill in the missing numbers.

2, _____, _____, _____, _____

There are _____ mittens altogether.

3.

One duck has _____ feet.

How many feet do 8 ducks have?

2, _____, _____, _____, _____, _____,

_____, _____

Eight ducks have _____ feet.

4. Count by 2's and fill in the blanks.

(a)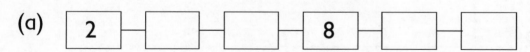

| 2 | | | 8 | | |

(b)

| | | | 18 | | 14 |

Unit 14 : Multiplication

Adding Equal Groups

When we multiply, we are adding equal groups.

These are equal groups.

(a)

4 + 4 = 8

2 fours = 8

(b)
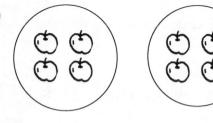 

There are 6 stars in each group.

There are 18 stars altogether.

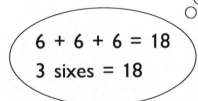

6 + 6 + 6 = 18

3 sixes = 18

Making Multiplication Stories

> 3 + 3 + 3 + 3 = 12
> 4 threes = 12

There are 4 groups of 3 caterpillars.

There are 12 caterpillars altogether.

We write the number sentence:

$4 \times 3 = 12$

> 4 threes is 12.

We say "4 times 3 equals 12."

'×' means 'multiply'.

Exercise 1 : Adding Equal Groups

1. Fill in the blanks.

(a)

$$5 + 5 + 5 = \text{_____}$$

$$3 \text{ fives} = \text{_____}$$

(b)

$$2 + 2 + 2 + 2 = \text{_____}$$

$$4 \text{ twos} = \text{_____}$$

(c)

There are _____ ducks in each group.

There are _____ ducks altogether.

(d)

There are _____ scouts in each group.

There are _____ scouts altogether.

(e)

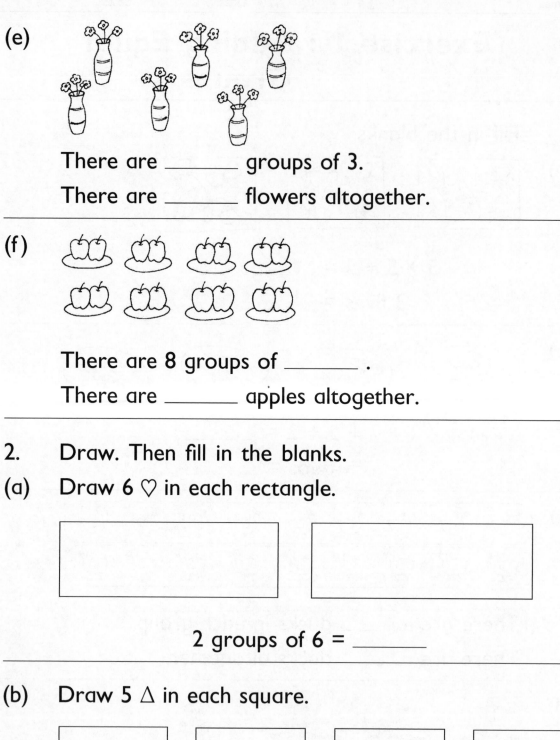

There are _____ groups of 3.

There are _____ flowers altogether.

(f)

There are **8** groups of _____ .

There are _____ apples altogether.

2. Draw. Then fill in the blanks.

(a) Draw 6 ♡ in each rectangle.

2 groups of 6 = _____

(b) Draw 5 △ in each square.

4 groups of 5 = _____

Primary Mathematics (Standards Edition) Extra Practice 1

Exercise 2 : Making Multiplication Stories

1. Fill in the blanks.

(a)

There are _____ children.

Each child has _____ books.

There are _____ books altogether.

We write _____ × _____ = _____.

(b)

There are _____ cakes.

Each cake has _____ candles.

There are _____ candles altogether.

We write _____ × _____ = _____ .

Exercise 3 : Multiplication Within 40

1. Match.

(4 sixes)   (5 sevens)   (3 twos)

| 3 × 2 | | 4 × 6 | | 5 × 7 |

| 5 groups of 7 | | Multiply 4 and 6 | | 3 groups of 2 |

2. Complete the multiplication sentences.

(a)

$$\boxed{} \times \boxed{} = 10$$

(b)

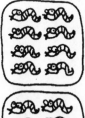

$$\boxed{} \times \boxed{} = 24$$

Primary Mathematics (Standards Edition) Extra Practice 1

(c)

$\boxed{} \times \boxed{} = \boxed{}$

(d)

$\boxed{} \times \boxed{} = \boxed{}$

(e)

$\boxed{} \times \boxed{} = \boxed{}$

(f)

$\boxed{} \times \boxed{} = \boxed{}$

3.   Draw.

(a)   Draw ✦ to show $4 \times 2 = 8$.

(b)   Draw ☺ to show $3 \times 3 = 9$.

Primary Mathematics (Standards Edition) Extra Practice 1

Unit 15 : Division

Friendly Notes

Meaning of Division

We share things in equal groups when we divide.

(a) There are 12 carrots.
We divide 12 carrots into 3 equal groups.
How many carrots are there in each group?

There are **4** carrots in each group.

We can also find how many equal groups there are when we divide.

We divide 12 carrots into groups of 4.
How many groups are there?

There are **3 groups** of 4.

(b) We divide 12 candles into groups of 3.
How many groups are there?

There are 4 groups.

(c) Pedro has 12 apples.
He wants to put 6 apples in one bag.
How many bags does he need?

He needs 2 bags.

(d) Share 15 mangoes equally among 3 girls.
How many mangoes does each girl get?

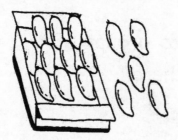

Each girl gets 5 mangoes.

Exercise 1 : Sharing and Grouping

1. Fill in the blanks.

(a)

The ladybugs are put equally in _____ groups.

There are _____ ladybugs in each group.

(b) Draw an equal number of candles for each cake.

There are _____ candles on each cake.

(c) Put 20 trees equally in 5 groups.

There are _____ trees in each group.

(d)   There are 24 orchids.

Circle the orchids in groups of 3.

There are _____ groups of 3.

(e)

There are 30 buttons.

Lindsey uses 6 buttons on one shirt.

She makes _____ shirts.

(f)

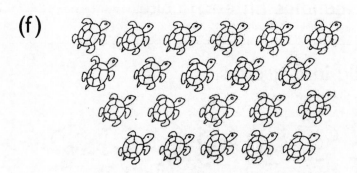

Dan has 21 turtles.

He puts 7 turtles in one tank.

He uses _____ tanks.

Primary Mathematics (Standards Edition) Extra Practice 1   © 2008 Marshall Cavendish International (Singapore) Private Limited

Unit 16 : Halves and Fourths

Friendly Notes

Halves

Half is 1 of 2 **equal** parts.
2 halves make **one whole**.

Each shape is divided into 2 equal parts.
Each part is a half.
Half of each shape is shaded.

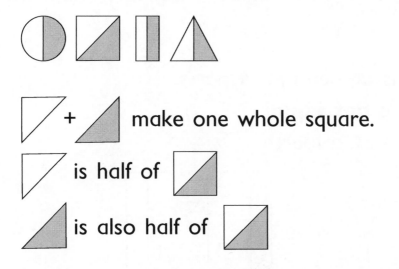

Each shape is divided into 2 parts.
The parts are **not equal**.
Each part is **not** a half.

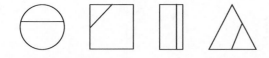

Fourths

A **fourth** is 1 of 4 **equal** parts.
4 fourths make **one whole**.

Each shape is divided into 4 equal parts.
Each part is a fourth.
A fourth of each shape is shaded.

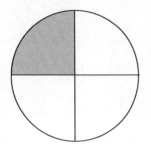 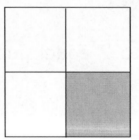 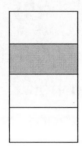 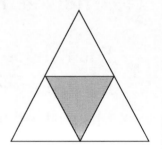

Each shape is divided into 4 parts.
The parts are **not equal**.
Each part is **not** a fourth.

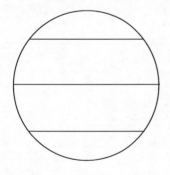 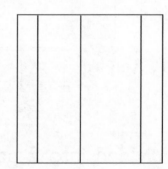

Exercise 1 : Making Halves and Fourths

1. Color the picture that shows halves.

(a)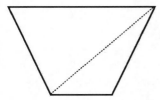

(b)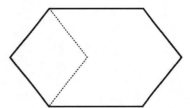

(c)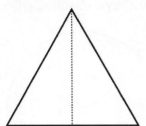

(d)

2. Color a half of each of the following shapes.

(a)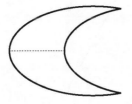

(b)

3. Check ☑ the shape that shows fourths.

(a)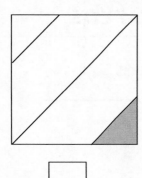

☐

(b)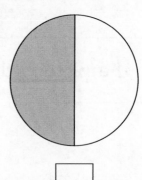

☐

(c)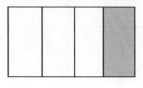

☐

(d)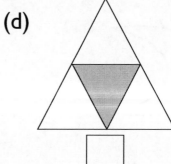

☐

4. Color a fourth of each of the following shapes.

(a)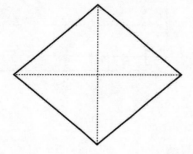

(b)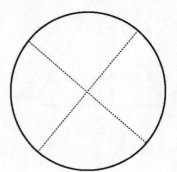

Unit 17 : Time

Friendly Notes

Telling and Estimating Time

We can tell the time by looking at the numbers on these clocks.

It is **3 o'clock**.
It is 3:00.

It is **not** 3 o'clock yet.
It is **almost** 3 o'clock.
It is **about** 3 o'clock.
It is **close** to 3 o'clock.
It is a **little before** 3 o'clock.

It is **after** 3 o'clock.
It is **a little after** 3 o'clock.

It is **half past 3**.

It is 3:30.

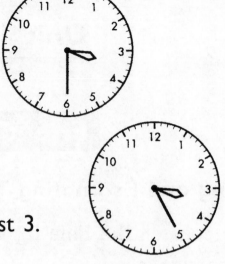

It is not half past 3 yet.

It is almost half past 3.

It is a little before half past 3.

It is about half past 3.

It is a little after half past 3.

Study these clocks. What time is it?

The time is 3:00.

The time is not 3:00.

It is after 12:00.

The time is 3:30.

The time is not 3:30.

It is after 6:00.

Primary Mathematics (Standards Edition) Extra Practice 1

Exercise 1A : Telling Time

1. **Match.**

| 12 o'clock |

| 2 o'clock |

| 6 o'clock |

| 4 o'clock |

---

2. **Match.**

| half past 1 |

| half past 7 |

| half past 9 |

| half past 6 |

3. **Write the time shown on each clock.**

(a)

3 o'clock

(b)

_____

(c)

_____

(d)

_____

(e)

_____

(f)

_____

(g)

_____

(h)

_____

Exercise 1B : Telling Time

1. Match.

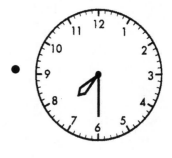

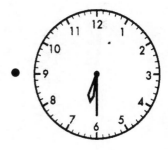

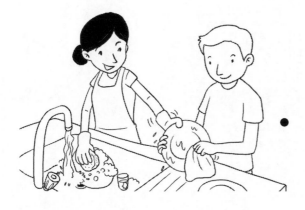

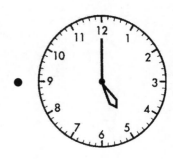

2. **Match.**

Primary Mathematics (Standards Edition) Extra Practice 1

© 2008 Marshall Cavendish International (Singapore) Private Limited

Exercise 2 : Estimating Time

1. Fill in the blanks.

(a)

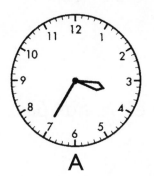

A

B

Clock _____ shows about half past three.

(b)

A

B

Clock _____ shows about nine o'clock.

(c)

A

B

Clock _____ shows about two o'clock.

2. Match.

   •   • about 7 o'clock

   •   • a little before half past nine

   •   • about half past twelve

   •   • a little after eleven o'clock

   •   • almost half past 5

3. Which takes longer?
    Check (✔) the answer.

    ☐ Brushing your teeth

    ☐ Eating dinner with your family

Primary Mathematics (Standards Edition) Extra Practice 1
© 2008 Marshall Cavendish International (Singapore) Private Limited

Unit 18 : Numbers to 100

Friendly Notes

Counting

Number	10	20	30	40	50	60	70	80	90	100
Number words	ten	twenty	thirty	forty	fifty	sixty	seventy	eighty	ninety	one hundred

Tens and Ones

62 = 6 tens 2 ones

74 = 7 tens 4 ones

98 = 9 tens 8 ones

We write 90 in words with an 'e': ninety

Write these numbers in words.

44 — forty-four

55 — fifty-five

62 — sixty-two

74 — seventy-four

98 — ninety-eight

Estimation

When we estimate, we make a reasonable guess how many of an object there are. To find out exactly how many there are, we count.

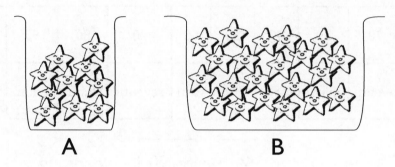

A   B

There are 10 stars in Jar A.

There are about 20 stars in Jar B.

Comparing and Ordering Numbers

We compare 2-digit numbers by comparing the tens first, then the ones.

54   **34**   **90**   **59**

Tens	Ones
5	4

Tens	Ones
3	4

Tens	Ones
9	0

Tens	Ones
5	9

9 tens is greater than 3 tens and 5 tens.

90 is the greatest.

3 tens is smaller than 9 tens and 5 tens.

34 is the smallest.

If the tens are the same, we compare the ones.

54 is 5 tens 4 ones.
59 is 5 tens 9 ones.

9 ones is greater than 4 ones.
59 is greater than 54.

Arrange these numbers in order: 54, 34, 90, 59
Begin with the smallest: 34, 54, 59, 90
Begin with the greatest: 90, 59, 54, 34

We use the sign **>** to show that one number **is greater than** the other.
We use the sign **<** to show that one number **is less than** the other.

| 54 | 34 | 90 | 59 |

90 is greater than 34.
90 > 34

54 is less than 59.
54 < 59

Addition Within 100

To add a 2-digit number and a 1-digit number, we can count on or add with number bonds.

72 + 4 = ?

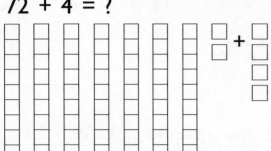 +

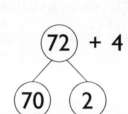

Count on 4 ones from 72: 73, 74, 75, 76

Step 1: Add 2 ones to 4 ones.
2 + 4 = 6

Step 2: Add 70 and 6.
70 + 6 = 76

So, 72 + 4 = 76.

We can also place the numbers one on top of the other and add as shown.

```
   72
+   4
─────
    6
```
Add the ones.
2 ones + 4 ones
= 6 ones

```
   72
+   4
─────
   76
```
Add the tens.
7 tens + 0 tens
= 7 tens

4 ones must be placed below 2 ones, not below 7 tens.

Primary Mathematics (Standards Edition) Extra Practice 1

To add a 2-digit number and a 1-digit number, we can also make a ten first.

78 + 4 = ?

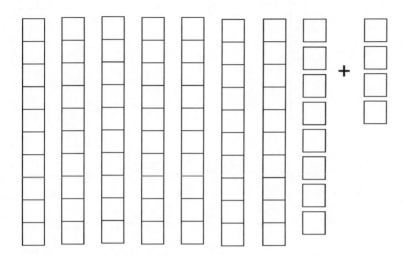

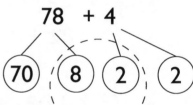

Step 1: Add 8 ones and 2 ones.
8 + 2 = 10

Step 2: Add 7 tens, 1 ten and 2 ones.
70 + 10 + 2 = 82

So, 78 + 4 = 82.

78 + 4 = 70 + 10 + 2 = 82

169

To add two 2-digit numbers, we can add the tens first.

72 + 14 = ?

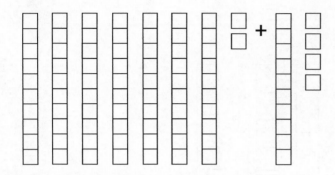

Step 1: Add 72 and 10.

72 + 10 = 82

72 + 14

(10) (4)

Step 2: Add 82 and 4.

82 + 4 = 86

72 + 14 = 72 + 10 + 4

So, 72 + 14 = 86.

We can also place the numbers one on top of the other and add as shown.

72	72
+ 14	+ 14
6	86

Add the ones.

2 ones + 4 ones

= 6 ones

Add the tens.

7 tens + 1 ten

= 8 tens

Subtraction Within 100

To subtract a **1-digit** number from a **2-digit** number, we can count backwards or subtract with number bonds.

59 – 7 = ?

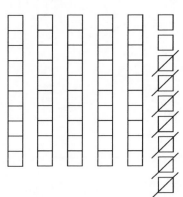

Count backwards 7 ones from 59: 58, 57, 56, 55, 54, 53, 52

Step 1: Subtract 7 ones from 9 ones.
9 – 7 = 2

59 – 7

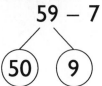

Step 2: Add 5 tens and 2 ones.
50 + 2 = 52

So, 59 – 7 = 52.

We can also place the numbers one on top of the other and subtract as shown.

59	59
– 7	– 7
2	52

Subtract the ones.

9 ones – 7 ones

= 2 ones

Subtract the tens.

5 tens – 0 tens

= 5 tens

To subtract a **1-digit** number from a **2-digit** number, sometimes we have to change 1 ten into 10 ones.

55 – 6 = ?

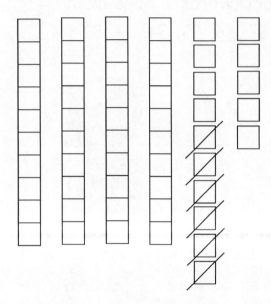

5 ones is less than 6 ones.
We cannot subtract 6 ones from 5 ones.
We change 1 ten into 10 ones.

Step 1: Subtract 6 from 15.
$$10 – 6 = 4$$

55 – 6

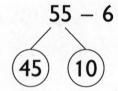

Step 2: Add 45 and 4.
$$45 + 4 = 49$$

So, 55 – 6 = 49.

Primary Mathematics (Standards Edition) Extra Practice 1

To subtract a 2-digit number from another 2-digit number, we can subtract the tens first.

54 – 23 = ?

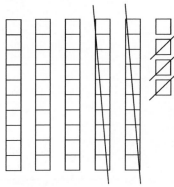

Step 1: Subtract 20 from 54.
54 – 20 = 34

Step 2: Subtract 3 from 34.
34 – 3 = 31

So, 54 – 23 = 31.

54 – 23

20   3

54 – 23 = 54 – 20 – 3

We can also place the numbers one on top of the other and subtract as shown.

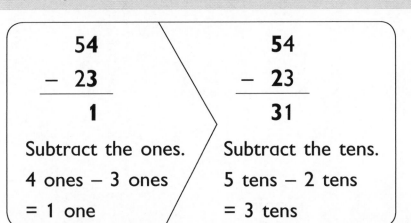

Subtract the ones.
4 ones – 3 ones
= 1 one

Subtract the tens.
5 tens – 2 tens
= 3 tens

Blank

Exercise 1 : Tens and Ones

1.   Match.

| 51 | 37 | 60 |

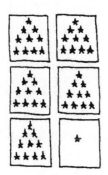      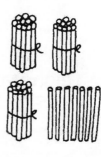

| thirty-seven | sixty | fifty-one |

2.   Fill in the boxes.

(a)

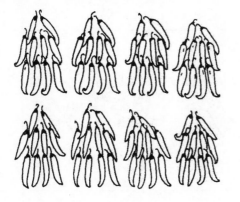

☐ tens ⇨ ☐

(b)

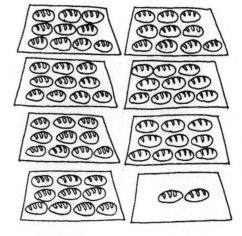

☐ tens ☐ ones ⇨ ☐

Primary Mathematics (Standards Edition) Extra Practice 1

3. Match.

| forty-five | ninety-nine | seventy-three |

(61) (54) (82) (73) (45) (99)

| eighty-two | fifty-four | sixty-one |

4. Write the correct number.

(a)

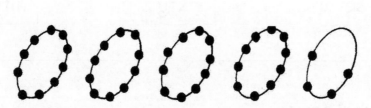

(b)

(c)

5. Write the numbers.

(a) twenty-seven _____   (b) forty-eight _____

(c) fifty _____   (d) thirty-six _____

(e) seventy-five _____   (f) eighty-three _____

(g) sixty-four _____   (h) thirty-nine _____

(i) one hundred _____   (j) ninety-one _____

6. Fill in the missing numbers in the number bonds.

(a)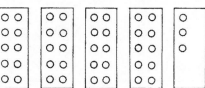

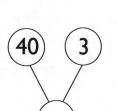

(b)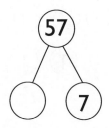

Primary Mathematics (Standards Edition) Extra Practice 1

7. Write how many tens and ones.
   Then, write the number in the box.

(a)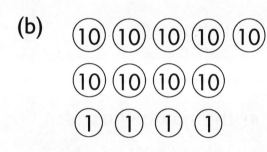

Tens	Ones

⇒ ☐

(b)

⑩ ⑩ ⑩ ⑩ ⑩
⑩ ⑩ ⑩ ⑩
① ① ① ①

Tens	Ones

⇒ ☐

(c)

⑩ ⑩ ⑩
① ① ① ①

Tens	Ones

⇒ ☐

Exercise 2 : Estimation

1.

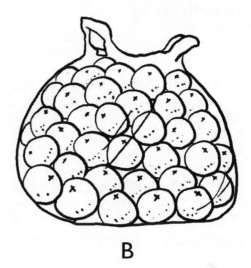

A   B

There are **16** oranges in Bag A.

(a)   There are about _____ oranges in
       Bag B.

(b)   There are about _____ oranges in both
       bags altogether.

Primary Mathematics (Standards Edition) Extra Practice 1

2.

(a) You can put about _____ pencils in your pencil case.

(b) You can skip about _____ times without stopping.

(c) You have about _____ friends at school.
You have exactly _____ friends at school.

Exercise 3 : Order of Numbers

1.   Fill in the blanks.

11			14			17			
	22			25					30
		33			36		38		
41			44					49	
	52			55		57			
		63			66				70

2.   Write the numbers in order. Begin with the given number.

(a)

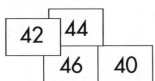

40 , ☐ , ☐ , ☐

The smallest number is _____.

The greatest number is _____.

(b)

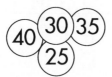

25 , ☐ , ☐ , ☐

The smallest number is _____.

The greatest number is _____.

(c)

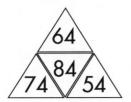

84 , ☐ , ☐ , ☐

The smallest number is _____.

The greatest number is _____ .

3. Fill in the blanks.

(a)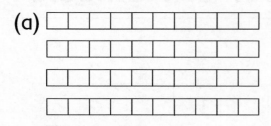

1 less than 41

is _____ .

10 less than 41

is _____ .

(b)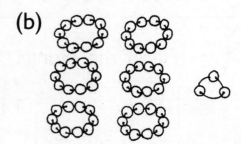

1 more than 63

is _____ .

10 more than 63

is _____ .

4. Fill in the missing numbers in the table.
Then fill in the blanks.

72			75	76				80
81			84		86			89	
91		93		95			98		

(a) 1 more than 74 is _____ .

(b) 1 less than 91 is _____ .

(c) 10 more than 87 is _____ .

(d) 10 less than 84 is _____ .

(e) 2 more than 90 is _____ .

(f) 20 less than 97 is _____ .

Exercise 4 : Comparing Numbers

1.   Fill in the circle with **>** or **<**.

(a)

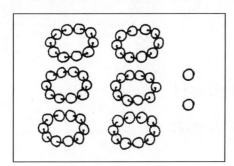 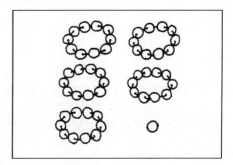

62 ◯ 51

(b)

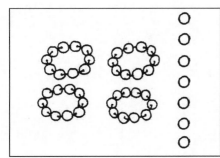 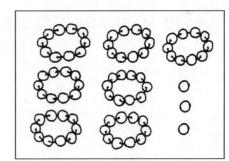

47 ◯ 73

(c)   88 ◯ 29

(d)   25 ◯ 52

(e)   95 ◯ 89

(f)   44 ◯ 64

2. Fill in the blanks.

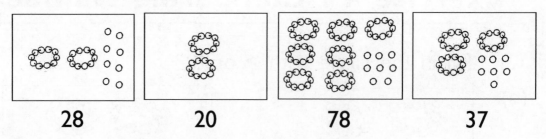

| 28 | 20 | 78 | 37 |

(a) Which number is the smallest? _____

(b) Which number is the greatest? _____

3. Arrange the numbers in order.
   Begin with the greatest.

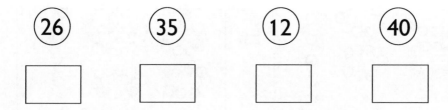

4. Arrange the numbers in order.
   Begin with the smallest.

Primary Mathematics (Standards Edition) Extra Practice 1

© 2008 Marshall Cavendish International (Singapore) Private Limited

Exercise 5 : Addition Within 100

1. Fill in the blanks.

(a)

34 + 3 = _____

(b)

47 + 6 = _____

2. Add.

(a)   4 + 2 = _____   (b)   1 + 3 = _____

      24 + 2 = _____   31 + 3 = _____

(c)   2 + 5 = _____   (d)   3 + 4 = _____

      42 + 5 = _____   43 + 4 = _____

(e)   7 + 3 = _____   (f)   8 + 5 = _____

      87 + 3 = _____   68 + 5 = _____

(g)   4 + 9 = _____   (h)   6 + 6 = _____

      44 + 9 = _____   56 + 6 = _____

3.   Add.

(a)   3 tens + 1 ten = _____ tens

        30 + 10 = _____

(b)   4 tens + 2 tens = _____ tens

        40 + 20 = _____

(c)   3 tens + 4 tens = _____ tens

        30 + 40 = _____

(d)   6 tens + 1 ten = _____ tens

        60 + 10 = _____

(e)   5 tens + 5 tens = _____ tens

        50 + 50 = _____

4.   Add.

(a)

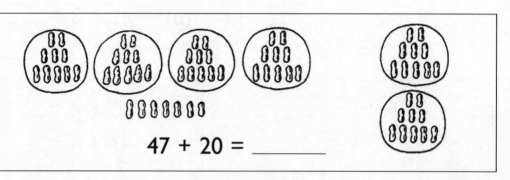

47 + 20 = _____

(b)

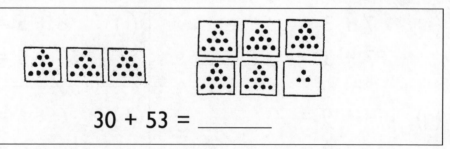

30 + 53 = _____

5. Add.

(a) 20 + 30 = _____

20 + 32 = _____

(b) 40 + 30 = _____

45 + 30 = _____

(c) 50 + 10 = _____

57 + 10 = _____

(d) 10 + 70 = _____

12 + 70 = _____

(e) 30 + 30 = _____

30 + 34 = _____

(f) 60 + 20 = _____

60 + 29 = _____

(g) 70 + 20 = _____

73 + 20 = _____

(h) 40 + 50 = _____

40 + 58 = _____

6. Add.

(a) 27 + 10 + 2 = _____

27 + 12 = _____

(b) 23 + 20 + 3 = _____

23 + 23 = _____

(c) 34 + 10 + 5 = _____

34 + 15 = _____

(d) 42 + 30 + 6 = _____

42 + 36 = _____

(e) 25 + 37 = _____

$$\begin{array}{r} 25 \\ +\ 37 \\ \hline \\ \hline \end{array}$$

(f) 38 + 48 = _____

(g) 56 + 29 = _____

(h) 69 + 31 = _____

Exercise 6 : Subtraction Within 100

1. Fill in the blanks.

(a)

$45 - 3 = \boxed{}$

(b)

$62 - 8 = \boxed{}$

2. Subtract.

(a) $7 - 2 =$ _____

$47 - 2 =$ _____

(b) $6 - 3 =$ _____

$56 - 3 =$ _____

(c) $12 - 8 =$ _____

$52 - 8 =$ _____

(d) $13 - 6 =$ _____

$63 - 6 =$ _____

(e) $11 - 7 =$ _____

$71 - 7 =$ _____

(f) $14 - 9 =$ _____

$84 - 9 =$ _____

(g) $15 - 8 =$ _____

$95 - 8 =$ _____

(h) $16 - 7 =$ _____

$66 - 7 =$ _____

3. Subtract.

(a) 6 tens – 5 tens = _____ ten

60 – 50 = _____

(b) 8 tens – 1 ten = _____ tens

80 – 10 = _____

(c) 9 tens – 6 tens = _____ tens

90 – 60 = _____

(d) 7 tens – 3 tens = _____ tens

70 – 30 = _____

(e) 10 tens – 8 tens = _____ tens

100 – 80 = _____

---

4. Subtract.

(a)

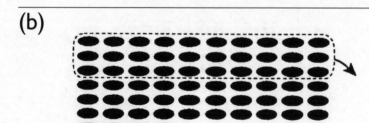

43 – 20 = _____

(b)

64 – 30 = _____

Primary Mathematics (Standards Edition) Extra Practice 1

5. Subtract.

(a) 20 − 10 = _____

27 − 10 = _____

(b) 40 − 30 = _____

49 − 30 = _____

(c) 50 − 20 = _____

55 − 20 = _____

(d) 60 − 10 = _____

64 − 10 = _____

(e) 70 − 40 = _____

72 − 40 = _____

(f) 80 − 20 = _____

86 − 20 = _____

(g) 90 − 50 = _____

98 − 50 = _____

(h) 90 − 60 = _____

91 − 60 = _____

6. Subtract.

(a) $36 - 10 - 3 =$ _____

    $36 - 13 =$ _____

(b) $45 - 10 - 4 =$ _____

    $45 - 14 =$ _____

(c) $48 - 20 - 7 =$ _____

    $48 - 27 =$ _____

(d) $57 - 20 - 2 =$ _____

    $57 - 22 =$ _____

(e) $52 - 38 =$ _____

$$\begin{array}{r} 52 \\ -\ 38 \\ \hline \\ \hline \end{array}$$

(f) $61 - 32 =$ _____

(g) $70 - 46 =$ _____

(h) $86 - 59 =$ _____

Unit 19 : Money

Value of Money

These are the coins and bills we use in the U.S.
We talk about the value of coins in cents (¢) and the value of bills in dollars ($).

Value of 1 coin/bill		We can change 1 of this for	How do we know this?
penny	1¢	—	—
nickel	5¢	5 pennies	Value of 5 pennies = 1¢ + 1¢ + 1¢ + 1¢ + 1¢
dime	10¢	10 pennies OR 2 nickels	Value of 10 pennies = 1¢ + 1¢ + 1¢ + 1¢ + 1¢ + 1¢ + 1¢ + 1¢ + 1¢ + 1¢ Value of 2 nickels = 5¢ + 5¢
quarter	25¢	25 pennies OR 5 nickels OR 2 dimes and 1 nickel	Value of 5 nickels = 5¢ + 5¢ + 5¢ + 5¢ + 5¢ Value of 2 dimes and 1 nickel = 10¢ + 10¢ + 5¢

193

half- dollar 	50¢	50 pennies OR 10 nickels OR 5 dimes OR 2 quarters	 Value of 10 nickels = 5¢ + 5¢ + 5¢ + 5¢ + 5¢ + 5¢ + 5¢ + 5¢ + 5¢ + 5¢ Value of 5 dimes = 10¢ + 10¢ + 10¢ + 10¢ + 10¢ Value of 2 quarters = 25¢ + 25¢
one dollar 	$1	2 half-dollars	Value of 2 half-dollars = 50¢ + 50¢
five dollars 	$5	5 one-dollar bills	Value of 5 one-dollar bills = $1 + $1 + $1 + $1 + $1
ten dollars 	$10	10 one-dollar bills OR 2 five-dollar bills	 Value of 2 five-dollar bills = $5 + $5

twenty dollars	$20	20 one-dollar bills	
		OR	
		2 ten-dollar bills	Value of 2 ten-dollar bills = $10 + $10
		OR	
		4 five-dollar bills	Value of 4 five-dollar bills = $5 + $5 + $5 + $5

How much money is there?

Which set has a greater amount of money?

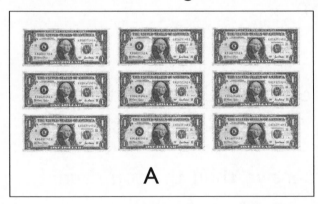

A

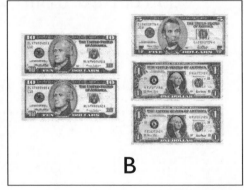

B

Set A has $9.
Set B has $27.

We add the **value** of the bills in each set, and **not the number of bills** in each set.

Set B has a greater amount of money.

We add or subtract to find the cost of things or how much more they cost than others.

Gwen has $15.
She wants to buy a doll and a toy drum.

(a) Which costs more? How much more?
(b) How much do the doll and toy drum cost altogether?
(c) How much more money does Gwen need to buy the doll and the toy drum?

(a) The doll costs more than the toy drum.
Subtract $8 from $10.
10 – 8 = 2

The doll costs $2 more than the toy drum.
The toy drum costs $2 less than the doll.

The doll is more expensive than the toy drum.
The toy drum is cheaper than the doll.

(b) 10 + 8 = 18
They cost $18 altogether.

(c) 18 – 15 = 3
Gwen needs $3 more.

Exercise 1 : Bills and Coins

1. Match.

(a)
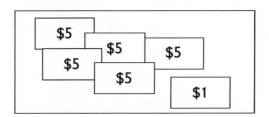

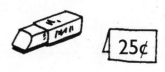 95¢

(b)
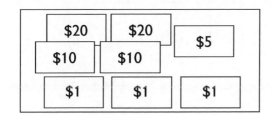

 25¢

(c)
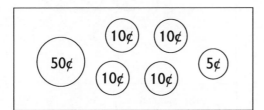

 45¢

(d)
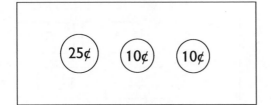

 $26

(e)
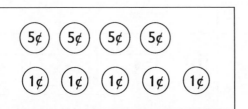

$68

(f)
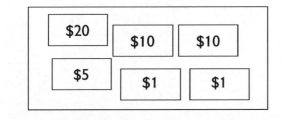

 $47

2. Write the amount of money in each set.

(a)

 25¢   10¢

5¢

[ ] ¢

(b)

50¢   25¢

5¢

[ ] ¢

(c)

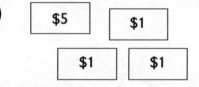 50¢   10¢ 10¢ 10¢   5¢ 5¢ 5¢

[ ] ¢

(d)

10¢ 10¢ 10¢

5¢ 5¢ 5¢ 1¢

5¢ 5¢ 1¢

[ ] ¢

(e)

$5 $1

$1 $1

$ [ ]

(f)

$5 $1 $1

$1 $1

$1 $1

$ [ ]

(g)

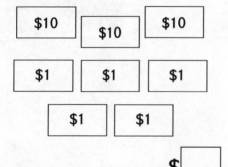 $10 $10 $10

$1 $1 $1

$1 $1

$ [ ]

(h)

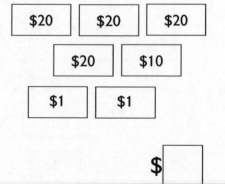 $20 $20 $20

$20 $10

$1 $1

$ [ ]

Primary Mathematics (Standards Edition) Extra Practice 1

© 2008 Marshall Cavendish International (Singapore) Private Limited

3. Check  the set that has more money.

4. Cross 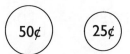 the set that has less money.

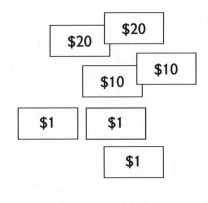

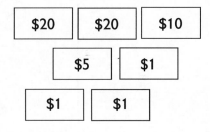

5. Check ✔ the set with the most amount of money.

Cross ✗ the set with the least amount of money.

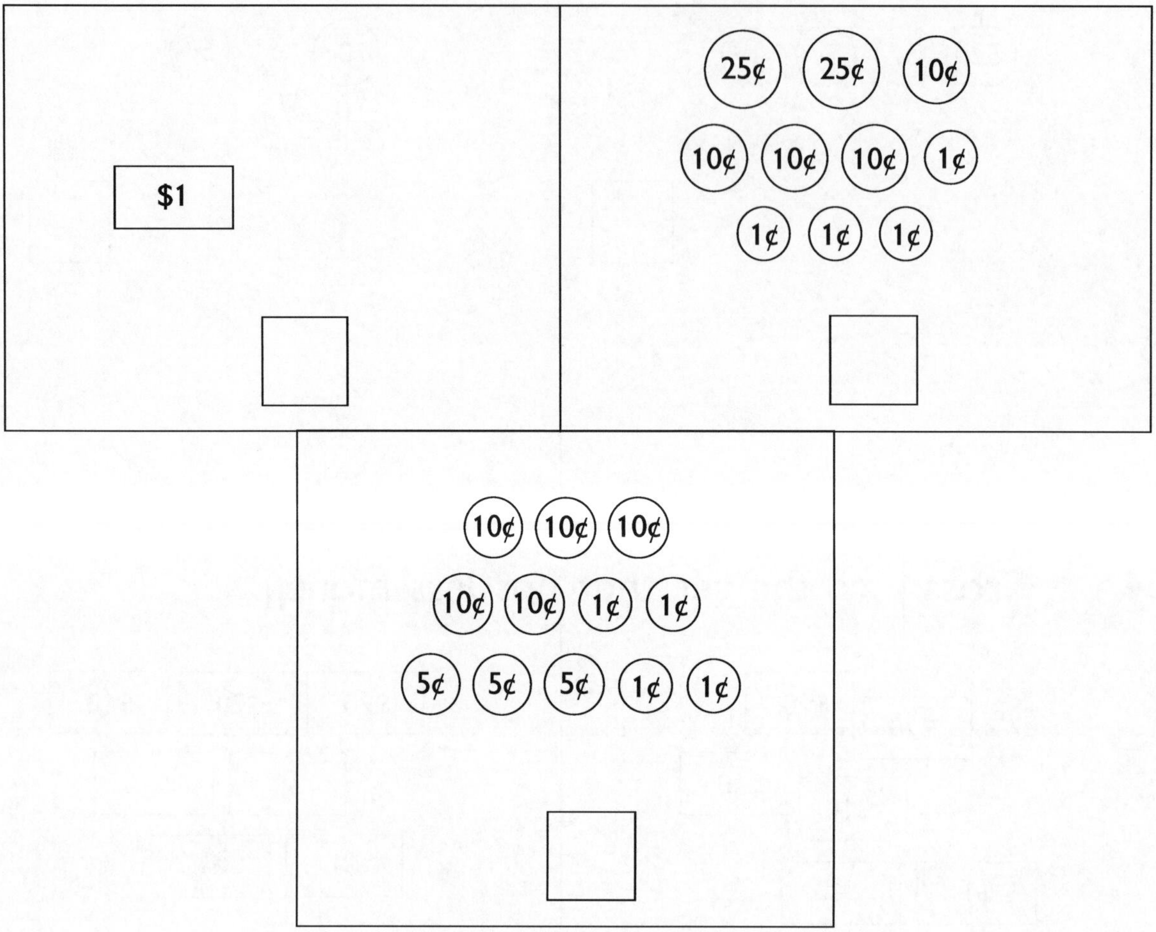

$1

25¢ 25¢ 10¢

10¢ 10¢ 10¢ 1¢

1¢ 1¢ 1¢

10¢ 10¢ 10¢

10¢ 10¢ 1¢ 1¢

5¢ 5¢ 5¢ 1¢ 1¢

Exercise 2 : Shopping

1.   Look at the pictures carefully. Then fill in the blanks.

(a)   Which costs more, the shoes or the sunglasses?
How much more?

The _____ cost $_____ more than the _____.

(b)   Fatimah bought the doll and the book.
How much did she pay?

She paid $_____.

(c)   Cameron had $5. He bought the sandwich.
How much money did he have left?

He had $_____ left.

Primary Mathematics (Standards Edition) Extra Practice 1

2.   Do these.

(a)   Ian paid 80¢ for the pair of scissors.

How much money did he get back?

He got _____¢ back.

(b)   Sally wants to buy this box of cookies.

If she has $1, how much more money

does she need?

She needs $_____ .

(c)   Emily bought the pencil and the ball-point pen.

How much did she spend?

She spent _____¢.

(d)   Amelia spent $27. Tyrone spent $52.

How much more money did Tyrone spend than Amelia?

Tyrone spent $_____ more than Amelia.

Unit 1 Numbers 0 to 10

Exercise 1A

1.

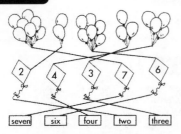

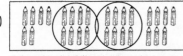

2. (a) 6   (b) 5   (c) 7   (d) 3

3. (a)

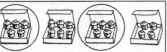

(b)

4.

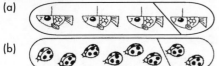

5.

Exercise 1B

2. (a)

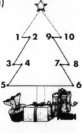

(b)

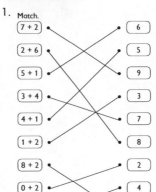

Unit 2 Number Bonds

Exercise 1

1. (a)

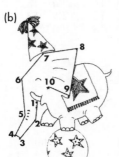

(b)

(c)

2. (a)

(b)

---

3. (a) 1   (b) 6   (c) 1   (d) 3
4. (a) 4   (b) 5   (c) 2   (d) 3   (e) 4   (f) 9
5. (a) 4   (b) 8   (c) 7   (d) 5
       (e) 5   (f) 8   (g) 3   (h) 3

Unit 3 Addition

Exercise 1

1. (a) 2, 3, 5   (b) 4, 4, 8   (c) 5, 2, 7
2. (a) 8   (b) 10   (c) 3, 7   (d) 2, 7

Exercise 2

1. (a) 6, 4   (b) 5, 3
      (c) 5, 5, 1, 4   (d) 6, 6, 4, 2
2. (a) 2, 7   (b) 2, 2
3. (a) 2, 3   (b) 5, 2
          3, 2   2, 5

Exercise 3A

1. (a) 9   (b) 5   (c) 6   (d) 10
      (e) 5   (f) 2   (g) 10   (h) 8
2. (a) 9   (b) 8   (c) 10   (d) 7
      (e) 7   (f) 9   (g) 10   (h) 7
      (i) 4   (j) 8   (k) 9   (l) 5
      (m) 8   (n) 8   (o) 10   (p) 5
3. (a) 6   (b) 5
4. (a) 10, 10   (b) 9, 9
5. (a) 4   (b) 9
6. (a) 6   (b) 8   (c) 7   (d) 6
      (e) 10

Exercise 3B

1. (a) 6, 6   (b) 3, 3   (c) 8, 8   (d) 9, 9
      (e) 10, 10

Exercise 3C

1. Match.

7 + 2	6
2 + 6	5
5 + 1	9
3 + 4	3
4 + 1	7
1 + 2	8
8 + 2	2
0 + 2	4
1 + 3	10

2. (a) 10   (b) 8   (c) 8   (d) 9
      (e) 9   (f) 10   (g) 1   (h) 10

Primary Mathematics (Standards Edition) Extra Practice 1

Unit 4 Subtraction

Exercise 1A

1. (a) 2, 5 (b) 1, 4 (c) 3 (d) 2
2. (a) 6, 4 (b) 5, 2
3. (a) 6, 6, 3 (b) 1, 3, 1, 2

Exercise 1B

1. (a) 5, 5 (b) 5, 5 (c) 3, 3 (d) –, 4, 4
   (e) –, 1, 1 (f) 9 – 5 = 4, 4 (g) 5 – 3 = 2, 2
   (h) 7 – 5 = 2, 2

Exercise 2A

1. (a) 5 (b) 3 (c) 0 (d) 1
   (e) 1 (f) 2 (g) 9 (h) 7
2. (a) 6 (b) 2 (c) 1 (d) 3
   (e) 3 (f) 2 (g) 2 (h) 0
   (i) 1 (j) 6 (k) 4 (l) 0
   (m) 3 (n) 2 (o) 6 (p) 6

Exercise 2B

1. (a) – (b) +
2. (a) + (b) + (c) – (d) –
3. (a) + (b) + (c) – (d) –
4. 5 + 4 = 9, 9 – 4 = 5, 4 + 5 = 9, 9 – 5 = 4
5. (a) 5 – 2 = 3 or 5 – 3 = 2
   (b) 4 + 6 = 10 or 6 + 4 = 10
   (c) 1 + 6 = 7 or 6 + 1 = 7
   (d) 8 – 0 = 8 or 8 – 8 = 0
6. (a) 6 (b) 6
7. (a) 4 (b) 5 (c) 3 (d) 6 (e) 1

Exercise 2C

1. Match.

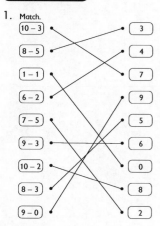

2. (a) 5 (b) 4 (c) 5 (d) 4
   (e) 4 (f) 3 (g) 0 (h) 2

Unit 5 Position

Exercise 1

1. (a) B (b) F (c) C (d) D
2. (a) 3 (b) 1, 4 (c) 1, 2, 1 (d) 2, 3 (e) 6, 4

Exercise 2

1.

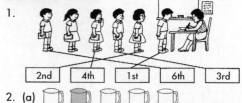

| 2nd | 4th | 1st | 6th | 3rd |

2. (a)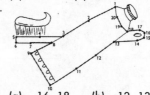

   (b) Color any 2 kites.

   (c)

   (d) Color any 4 rulers.

3. (a)

   (b)

Unit 6 Numbers to 20

Exercise 1

1. (a) 13 (b) 11 (c) 12 (d) 20
   (e) 16 (f) 19
2. (a) 13 (b) 17
3. (a) 11 (b) 16 (c) 12 (d) 17
   (e) 13 (f) 18 (g) 14 (h) 19
4. (a) 15 (b) 18 (c) 10, 4 (d) 10, 7
5. (a) 16 (b) 19
6.

7. (a) 16, 18 (b) 12, 13 (c) 20, 17, 16
8. (a) 11 (b) 13 (c) 14
9. (a) 18 (b) 15
10. 9, 10, 11, 12, 13, 14
11. 11, 14, 15, 18, 20
12. 19, 16, 12, 7, 4

Exercise 2A

1. (a) 14 (b) 19 (c) 17 (d) 15
   (e) 11 (f) 15 (g) 12 (h) 12
2. (a) 19 (b) 20 (c) 17 (d) 16
   (e) 20 (f) 16 (g) 17 (h) 18

Exercise 2B

1. (a) 4   (b) 8   (c) 12   (d) 10
   (e) 12   (f) 15   (g) 4   (h) 8
2. (a) 6   (b) 9   (c) 3   (d) 10
   (e) 8   (f) 7   (g) 6   (h) 8

Exercise 2C

1. (a) –   (b) –   (c) +   (d) –   (e) –
   (f) +   (g) +   (h) –   (i) –   (j) +
2. (a) 13 − 6 = 7   or   13 − 7 = 6
   (b) 10 + 10 = 20
   (c) 12 + 6 = 18   or   6 + 12 = 18
   (d) 17 − 1 = 16   or   17 − 16 = 1
3. (a) 4 + 7 = 11   7 + 4 = 11
     11 − 4 = 7   11 − 7 = 4
   (b) 8 + 6 = 14   6 + 8 = 14
     14 − 6 = 8   14 − 8 = 6

Exercise 2D

1. (a) 16   (b) 18   (c) 11
   (d) 13   (e) 11   (f) 14
2.

   7 + 5   7 + 4
   2 + 9   9 + 4
   8 + 7   6 + 6
   7 + 6   8 + 9
   9 + 8   6 + 9
   10 + 8   9 + 9
   9 + 7   8 + 6
   7 + 7   10 + 6

3.

   11 − 4   11
   19 − 8   8
   15 − 9   4
   14 − 6   6
   12 − 8   9
   16 − 7   7
   12 − 9   10
   17 − 7   3

4. (a) 14   (b) 14   (c) 3   (d) 5
   (e) 8   (f) 8   (g) 5   (h) 8

Unit 7 Shapes

Exercise 1A

1. (a)   (b)   (c)
   (d)   (e)   (f)

2. (a)

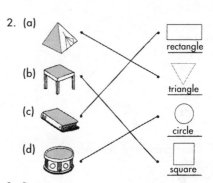

3. B
4. B
5. (a) check books and rulers
   (b) check marbles and glasses
   (c) check cubes and toy aeroplanes

Exercise 1B

3. (a)   (b)   (c)   (d)   (e)

Unit 8 Length

Exercise 1

2. (a)   (b)

3. (a) C   (b) B   (c) B   (d) D

Exercise 2

1. (a) 6   (b) 3
2. (a) 6   (b) 4   (c) 6
3. (a) 6   (b) 3   (c) 2   (d) 4

Unit 9 Weight

Exercise 1

1. (a) lighter than (b) as heavy as
   (c) heavier than (d) lighter than

Exercise 2

1. (a) 6 (b) 5 (c) B (d) C (e) C
2. (a) 5 (b) 10 (c) banana (d) banana
   (e) cabbage

Unit 10 Capacity

Exercise 1

1. Circle the pot.
2. Circle the bottle.
3. (a) No (b) Yes (c) Yes (d) No
4. A

Exercise 2

1. (a) C (b) 2 (c) 5
2. (a) A, B (b) A, 3, B

Unit 11 Comparing Numbers

Exercise 1A

1. (a) No (b) No (c) Yes (d) Yes
2. (a) 7 (b) 4
3. (a) 9 (b) 5

Exercise 1B

1.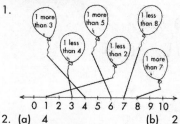

2. (a) 4 (b) 2
3. (a) Paula, 6 (b) Robert, 5

Exercise 2

1. (a) 2, 2 (b) 3, 3 (c) 6, 6, 6

Unit 12 Graphs

Exercise 1A

1. (a) 8 (b) cars (c) 3 (d) 2
2. (a) 5 (b) Wendy (c) Tyrone (d) 13
3. (a) 17 (b) apples (c) 3 (d) 6
4. (a) 5 (b) 3 (c) dolls (d) robot (e) toy car

Exercise 1B

1. 4,5,5 (a) 4 (b) 5 (c) 5 (d) 14
2.

Type of Fruit	Number of Fruit	Total
Bananas	//// ///	8
Oranges	////	5
Pears	//// ////	9
Apples	////	4

   (a) Pears (b) Yes
3. (a) 4 boxes (b) 3 boxes (c) 5 boxes (d) 2 boxes
4. Bar graph

5. (a) 5 (b) cookies (c) 2
6.

Carrots	///
Cookies	////
Apples	////

Unit 13 Numbers to 40

Exercise 1A

1. (a) 25 (b) 33
2.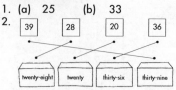

3. (a) 23 (b) 35 (c) 29 (d) 31 (e) 37
   (f) 40 (g) 26 (h) 34
4. (a) 22, 26, 28, 30
   (b) 38, 35, 34, 32

Exercise 1B

1. (a) 24 (b) 32
2. (a) 7 (b) 30 (c) 34
3. 3, 4, 7, 9, 12, 14, 15, 17, 18, 20, 22,
   23, 25, 26, 28, 29, 31, 33, 34, 36, 38, 39
4. (a) 27 (b) 29 (c) 20 (d) 33
5. (a) 18 (b) 37 (c) 37 (d) 18

Exercise 2

1. (a) 2, 7 (b) 3, 4
2. (a) 2, 3, 23 (b) 3, 5, 35 (c) 3, 3, 33
3. (a) 30, 39 (b) 23, 14 (c) 33, 42
   (d) 34, 25

Exercise 3A

1. (a) 28 (b) 36 (c) 30 (d) 25
   (e) 39 (f) 36 (g) 21 (h) 32
   (i) 35 (j) 34 (k) 25 (l) 31
2. (a) 5, 15 (b) 4, 14 (c) 9, 29 (d) 9, 29
   (e) 8, 38 (f) 8, 38 (g) 12, 22 (h) 13, 33
   (i) 12, 22 (j) 15, 35 (k) 14, 34 (l) 10, 40

Exercise 3B

1. (a) 12 (b) 28 (c) 35 (d) 23
   (e) 19 (f) 34 (g) 39 (h) 26
   (i) 17 (j) 15 (k) 21 (l) 38
2. (a) 1, 21 (b) 3, 23 (c) 1, 31 (d) 4, 34
   (e) 2, 32 (f) 3, 23 (g) 7, 17 (h) 7, 17
   (i) 9, 29 (j) 8, 28 (k) 7, 17 (l) 9, 29
3. (a)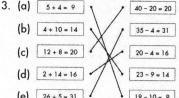

   (b)
   (c)
   (d)
   (e)
   (f)
   (g)
   (h)
   (i)
   (j)

Primary Mathematics (Standards Edition) Extra Practice 1

Exercise 4

1. (a) 9　　(b) 9　　(c) 15　　(d) 20
2. (a) a. 18　b. 18　c. 8　d. 13　e. 12　f. 19
　 (b) a. 20　b. 10　c. 15　d. 14　e. 12　f. 19

Exercise 5

1. 2, 4, 6, 8, 10, 12, 14, 16, 18, 20
2. 4, 6, 8, 10; 10
3. 2; 4, 6, 8, 10, 12, 14, 16, 16
4. (a)　4, 6, 10, 12,
　 (b)　24, 22, 20, 16

Unit 14 Multiplication

Exercise 1

1. (a)　15, 15　(b)　8, 8　(c)　9, 18　(d)　3, 12
　 (e)　6, 18　(f)　2, 16
2. (a) ♡ ♡ ♡ ♡ ♡ ♡　♡ ♡ ♡ ♡ ♡ ♡　12
　 (b) △△ △△ △△ △△
　　　 △△△ △△△ △△△ △△△　20

Exercise 2

1. (a)　4, 2, 8, 4 × 2 = 8
　 (b)　5, 3, 15, 5 × 3 = 15

Exercise 3

1.
| 4 sixes | 5 sevens | 3 twos |

| 3 × 2 | 4 × 6 | 5 × 7 |

| 5 groups of 7 | Multiply 4 and 6 | 3 groups of 2 |

2. (a)　2, 5　　　(b)　3, 8　　　(c)　3, 4, 12
　 (d)　7, 2, 14　(e)　6, 3, 18　(f)　5, 5, 25
3. (a)　　　　　(b)

Unit 15 Division

Exercise 1

1. (a)　3, 5　(b)　4　(c)　4　(d)　8
　 (e)　5　　(f)　3

Unit 16 Halves and Fourths

Exercise 1

1. (c)　　and (d)

2. (a)　　and (b)

3. Check 3(c) and 3(d)
4. (a)　　　　　(b)

Unit 17 Time

Exercise 1A

1.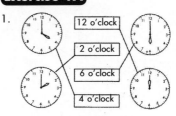
| 12 o'clock |
| 2 o'clock |
| 6 o'clock |
| 4 o'clock |

2.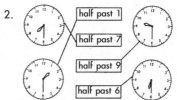
| half past 1 |
| half past 7 |
| half past 9 |
| half past 6 |

3. (a)　3 o'clock　　　　　(b)　5 o'clock
　 (c)　9 o'clock　　　　　(d)　half past 8
　 (e)　half past 12　　　(f)　half past 10
　 (g)　7 o'clock　　　　　(h)　half past 4

Exercise 1B

1.

2.

Exercise 2

1. (a)　A　　　(b)　B　　　(c)　B

Exercise 1B

1.

2.

Exercise 2

1. (a) A   (b) B   (c) B

2.

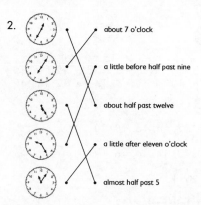

a little before half past nine

about half past twelve

a little after eleven o'clock

almost half past 5

about 7 o'clock

3. Check box 'eating dinner with your family'.

Unit 18 Numbers to 100

Exercise 1

1.

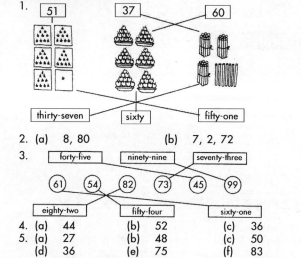

| 51 | | 37 | | 60 |

thirty-seven   sixty   fifty-one

2. (a) 8, 80   (b) 7, 2, 72

3. forty-five   ninety-nine   seventy-three

61   54   82   73   45   99

eighty-two   fifty-four   sixty-one

4.	(a)	44	(b)	52	(c)	36
5.	(a)	27	(b)	48	(c)	50
	(d)	36	(e)	75	(f)	83
	(g)	64	(h)	39	(i)	100
	(j)	91				
6.	(a)	43	(b)	50		
7.	(a)	6, 5, 65	(b)	9, 4, 94	(c)	3, 4, 34

Exercise 2

1. (a), (b) answers vary
2. (a), (b), (c) answers vary

Exercise 3

1. 12, 13, 15, 16, 18, 19, 20
   21, 23, 24, 26, 27, 28, 29
   31, 32, 34, 35, 37, 39, 40
   42, 43, 45, 46, 47, 48, 50
   51, 53, 54, 56, 58, 59, 60
   61, 62, 64, 65, 67, 68, 69
2. (a)   42, 44, 46, 40, 46
   (b)   30, 35, 40, 25, 40
   (c)   74, 64, 54, 54, 84
3. (a)   40, 31   (b)   64, 73
4. 73, 74, 77, 78, 79, 82, 83, 85, 87, 88, 90,
   92, 94, 96, 97, 99, 100
   (a) 75   (b) 90   (c) 97   (d) 74
   (e) 92   (f) 77

Exercise 4

1. (a) >   (b) <   (c) >
   (d) <   (e) >   (f) <
2. (a) 20   (b) 78
3. 40, 35, 26, 12
4. 29, 36, 63, 92

Exercise 5

1. (a) 37   (b) 53
2. (a) 6, 26 (b) 4, 34 (c) 7, 47 (d) 7, 47
   (e) 10, 90 (f) 13, 73 (g) 13, 53 (h) 12, 62
3. (a) 4, 40 (b) 6, 60 (c) 7, 70 (d) 7, 70
   (e) 10, 100
4. (a) 67   (b) 83
5. (a) 50, 52 (b) 70, 75 (c) 60, 67 (d) 80, 82
   (e) 60, 64 (f) 80, 89 (g) 90, 93 (h) 90, 98
6. (a) 39, 39 (b) 46, 46 (c) 49, 49 (d) 78, 78
   (e) 62, 62 (f) 86   (g) 85   (h) 100

Exercise 6

1. (a) 42   (b) 54
2. (a) 5, 45 (b) 3, 53 (c) 4, 44 (d) 7, 57
   (e) 4, 64 (f) 5, 75 (g) 7, 87 (h) 9, 59
3. (a) 1, 10 (b) 7, 70 (c) 3, 30 (d) 4, 40
   (e) 2, 20
4. (a) 23   (b) 34
5. (a) 10, 17 (b) 10, 19 (c) 30, 35   (d)
        50, 54
   (e) 30, 32 (f) 60, 66 (g) 40, 48 (h) 30, 31
6. (a) 23, 23 (b) 31, 31 (c) 21, 21 (d) 35, 35
   (e) 14, 14 (f) 29   (g) 24   (h) 27

Unit 19 Money

Exercise 1A

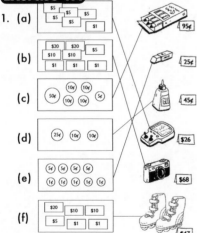

1. (a)
   (b)
   (c)
   (d)
   (e)
   (f)

2. (a) 40   (b) 80   (c) 95   (d) 57
   (e) 8   (f) 11   (g) 35   (h) 92
3. Check the set with 91¢
4. Cross the set that has $58
5. Tick the set with $1
   Cross the set with 69¢

Exercise 2

1. (a) 32 − 29 = 3, sunglasses, 3, shoes
   (b) 12 + 4 = 16, 16   (c) 5 − 2 = 3, 3
2. (a) 80 − 65 = 15, 15   (b) 3 − 1 = 2, 2
   (c) 25 + 55 = 80, 80   (d) 52 − 27 = 25, 25

209

Blank